WeightWatchers®

Ultimate
Flex & Core
Cookbook

A Word About Weight Watchers

Since 1963, Weight Watchers has grown from a handful of members to millions of enrollments annually. Today Weight Watchers is recognized as the leading name in safe and sensible weight control. Weight Watchers members are a diverse group, from youths to senior citizens, attending meetings virtually around the globe. Weight-loss and weight-management results vary by individual, but we recommend that you attend Weight Watchers meetings, follow the Weight Watchers food plan, and participate in regular physical activity. For the Weight Watchers meeting nearest you, call **800-651-6000**. Also, visit us at our Web site, **WeightWatchers.com**, or look for *Weight Watchers* Magazine at your newsstand or in your meeting room.

 **CORE PLAN** RECIPE   NO COOK   🕐 20 MINUTES OR LESS   🥕 VEGETARIAN

Pan-Seared Scallops with
Melon Salsa, page 205

WEIGHT WATCHERS PUBLISHING GROUP

CREATIVE AND EDITORIAL DIRECTOR	**NANCY GAGLIARDI**
ART DIRECTOR	**ED MELNITSKY**
PRODUCTION MANAGER	**ALAN BIEDERMAN**
ASSOCIATE ART DIRECTOR	**JENNIFER BOWLES**
OFFICE MANAGER AND PUBLISHING ASSISTANT	**JENNY LABOY-BRACE**
FOOD EDITOR	**EILEEN RUNYAN**
FOOD CONSULTANT	**CAROL PRAGER**
RECIPE DEVELOPERS	**DAVID BONOM** **MARK SCARBROUGH** **BRUCE WEINSTEIN**
NUTRITION CONSULTANT	**U. BEATE KRINKE**
PHOTOGRAPHER	**ANN STRATTON**
FOOD STYLIST	**MICHAEL PEDERSON**
PROP STYLIST	**BETTE BLAU**
DESIGN/PRODUCTION	**LYNDA D'AMICO**

ON THE COVER: Warm White Bean Salad, page 26 (with a *POINTS*® value of only 2)

About Our Recipes

We make every effort to ensure that you will have success with our recipes. For best results and for nutritional accuracy, please keep the following guidelines in mind:

● Recipes in this book have been developed for Weight Watchers members who are following either the **Core Plan** or the **Flex Plan** on the TurnAround™ program. All **Core Plan** recipes are marked with our **Core Plan** recipe icon ☑. We include *POINTS*® values so you can use any of the recipes if you are following the **Flex Plan** on the program. *POINTS* values are assigned based on calories, fat (grams), and fiber (grams) provided for a serving size of a recipe.

● All recipes feature approximate nutritional information; our recipes are analyzed for Calories (Cal), Total Fat (Fat), Saturated Fat (Sat Fat), Trans Fat (Trans Fat), Cholesterol (Chol), Sodium (Sod), Carbohydrates (Carb), Dietary Fiber (Fib), Protein (Prot), and Calcium (Calc).

● Nutritional information for recipes that include meat, poultry, and fish are based on cooked skinless boneless portions (unless otherwise stated), with the fat trimmed.

● We recommend that you buy lean meat and poultry, then trim it of all visible fat before cooking. When poultry is cooked with the skin on, we suggest removing the skin before eating.

● Before serving, divide foods—including any vegetables, sauce, or accompaniments—into portions of equal size according to the designated number of servings per recipe.

● Any substitutions made to the ingredients will alter the "Per serving" nutritional information and may affect the **Core Plan** recipe status or the *POINTS* value.

● It is implied that all fresh fruits, vegetables, and greens in recipes should be rinsed before using.

Broiled Cheese, Bread, and
Bean Soup , page 49

Contents

CHAPTER 1

Small Plates and Other Starters

Romaine, Turkey, and Roasted Pepper Wraps

PREP	15 MINUTES
COOK	NONE
SERVES	4

1 Place the lettuce leaves on a board, cupped-side up, with the root ends toward you. Onto each leaf, place one slice of the turkey. Spread each with ¼ teaspoon of the mustard. Divide the roasted peppers, parsley, and ground pepper among the leaves.

2 One at a time, fold in the sides of each filled leaf. Then, starting at the root end, roll up and secure with a toothpick, if needed.

PER SERVING (2 rolls): 105 Cal, 1 g Fat, 0 g Sat Fat, 0 g Trans Fat, 47 mg Chol, 208 mg Sod, 7 g Carb, 1 g Fib, 18 g Prot, 24 mg Calc. **POINTS** value: **2.**

EXPRESS LANE Make an extra batch of rolls for an instant snack later in the week. Wrap each roll in plastic wrap and refrigerate up to 2 days.

8 large **romaine lettuce leaves**, tough part of stalks removed

8 (1-ounce) slices **roasted turkey breast**

2 teaspoons **Dijon mustard**

1 (12-ounce) jar **roasted red bell peppers** (not in oil), drained and sliced into 8 strips

¼ cup chopped fresh **flat-leaf parsley** or **basil**

½ teaspoon freshly **ground pepper**

Smoked Salmon Rolls with Creamy Chive Filling

PREP	25 MINUTES PLUS 1½ HOURS CHILLING TIME
COOK	NONE
SERVES	4

¼ pound thinly sliced **smoked salmon**

½ cup **yogurt cheese** (see below)

¼ cup finely chopped **fresh chives** or **dill**

Freshly **ground pepper**, to taste

1 small bunch **chives**

1 **lemon**, cut into 8 wedges

1 Gently separate and line up the slices of salmon to make 8 pieces, about 5 inches long; lay out on wax paper or plastic wrap and set aside.

2 Combine the yogurt cheese and chopped chives in a small bowl. Place 1 tablespoon of the mixture on one end of each salmon slice. Gently roll up, then sprinkle rolls with pepper.

3 Arrange the salmon rolls on a chilled serving platter. Serve at once or cover with plastic wrap and refrigerate up to 4 hours. Garnish with the whole chives and lemon wedges.

PER SERVING (2 rolls): 74 Cal, 1 g Fat, 0 g Sat Fat, 0 g Trans Fat, 8 mg Chol, 270 mg Sod, 6 g Carb, 1 g Fib, 9 g Prot, 136 mg Calc. ***POINTS*** value: *1*.

HOW WE DID IT To make yogurt cheese, place 1 cup plain fat-free yogurt in a sieve lined with a damp paper towel over a bowl. Refrigerate, covered with plastic wrap, 1½ hours or overnight. Discard the liquid in the bowl. Makes ½ cup yogurt cheese.

Devils on Horseback

Devils on Horseback

PREP	10 MINUTES
COOK	ABOUT 4 MINUTES
SERVES	6

1 Spray a broiler rack with nonstick spray; preheat broiler.

2 Cut a slit lengthwise in each prune; spoon ½ teaspoon of the chopped olives into each cavity. Wrap the prunes in the bacon and secure with wooden toothpicks.

3 Arrange the prunes on the broiler rack and broil 3 inches from the heat until the bacon is crisp, about 2 minutes on each side.

PER SERVING (2 pieces): 76 Cal, 3 g Fat, 1 g Sat Fat, 0 g Trans Fat, 8 mg Chol, 244 mg Sod, 11 g Carb, 1 g Fib, 2 g Prot, 12 mg Calc. **POINTS** value: *2.*

FOOD NOTE Be aware that when shopping for prunes at the supermarket, many brands are now labeled "dried plums." Both products can be used interchangeably.

12 **pitted prunes**

2 tablespoons chopped **pimiento-stuffed green olives**

6 slices **turkey bacon**, halved crosswise

Green Goddess Dip

PREP	15 MINUTES
COOK	NONE
SERVES	8

Puree ½ cup of the sour cream, the yogurt, parsley, scallions, tarragon, anchovy paste, and lemon juice in a blender. Transfer to a small bowl; gently stir in the remaining sour cream, the salt, and pepper.

PER SERVING (scant ¼ cup): 53 Cal, 4 g Fat, 2 g Sat Fat, 0 g Trans Fat, 12 mg Chol, 147 mg Sod, 3 g Carb, 0 g Fib, 2 g Prot, 69 mg Calc. *POINTS* value: *1*.

HOW WE DID IT Our substitute of light sour cream and plain low-fat yogurt in this dip results in a much cleaner flavor than the traditional high-calorie version. But overmixing sour cream in a blender or food processor can make it watery. So we suggest stirring in half of the sour cream at the end to keep the dip a thicker consistency.

1 (8-ounce) container **light sour cream**

½ cup plain **low-fat yogurt**

½ cup firmly packed **flat-leaf parsley** leaves

2 **scallions**, sliced

2 tablespoons **fresh tarragon leaves**

1 teaspoon **anchovy paste**

1 teaspoon **fresh lemon juice**

¼ teaspoon **salt**

¼ teaspoon freshly **ground pepper**

Tonnato Dip

PREP	20 MINUTES PLUS 2 HOURS CHILLING TIME
COOK	NONE
SERVES	4

Put all the ingredients in a food processor or blender; process until smooth, about 2 minutes. Transfer to a serving dish. Cover and refrigerate until chilled, at least 2 hours or up to 2 days.

PER SERVING (¼ cup): 85 Cal, 4 g Fat, 1 g Sat Fat, 0 g Trans Fat, 18 mg Chol, 469 mg Sod, 5 g Carb, 1 g Fib, 9 g Prot, 9 mg Calc. *POINTS* value: *2.*

FOOD NOTE Serve this dip with colorful bell pepper strips and cucumber slices. Or, for another tasty dunker, add cubes of roasted pork tenderloin precooked from the supermarket deli (1 ounce for each serving will increase the *POINTS* value by 1).

1 (6-ounce) can **solid white tuna in water**, drained and flaked

½ cup **fat-free mayonnaise**

2 tablespoons **fresh lemon juice**

1½ tablespoons drained **capers**

1½ teaspoons **extra-virgin olive oil**

Creamy Red Pepper-Herb Dip

PREP	15 MINUTES
COOK	NONE
SERVES	12

Puree the cream cheese, roasted peppers, garlic, salt, and ground pepper in a food processor. Transfer the mixture to a medium bowl, then stir in the chives and thyme.

PER SERVING (2 tablespoons): 52 Cal, 4 g Fat, 3 g Sat Fat, 0 g Trans Fat, 14 mg Chol, 141 mg Sod, 1 g Carb, 0 g Fib, 2 g Prot, 16 mg Calc.
POINTS value: *1.*

EXPRESS LANE To save time, you can use jarred minced garlic instead of crushing or mincing your own. Jarred garlic is available in the produce section of most supermarkets; it's a convenience product perfect for quick cooking. Be sure to buy only minced garlic or minced garlic preserved in water—not minced garlic packed in oil. Once opened, store in the refrigerator and discard when the garlic begins to turn brown, after about 2 months.

1 (8-ounce) package **light cream cheese** (Neufchâtel)

½ cup jarred **roasted red bell peppers**, drained

1 small **garlic** clove, crushed with a press

¼ teaspoon **salt**

⅛ teaspoon freshly **ground pepper**

¼ cup snipped **fresh chives**

½ teaspoon chopped **fresh thyme**

Cajun-Spiced Shrimp Cocktail
with Mango Salsa

PREP	30 MINUTES
COOK	ABOUT 10 MINUTES
SERVES	12

1 To make the salsa, combine the mango, bell pepper, onion, cilantro, lime juice, salt, and ground pepper in a medium bowl; set aside.

2 Place the Cajun seasoning in a small bowl. Dip each shrimp into the seasoning to coat. Heat 1½ teaspoons of the oil in a large nonstick skillet over medium-high heat. Add half of the shrimp and cook until just opaque in the center, about 2 minutes on each side. Transfer to a plate. Repeat with the remaining shrimp and oil. Serve the shrimp at once with the salsa or let the shrimp cool to room temperature.

PER SERVING (3 shrimp with 2½ tablespoons salsa): 50 Cal, 1 g Fat, 0 g Sat Fat, 0 g Trans Fat, 51 mg Chol, 284 mg Sod, 4 g Carb, 0 g Fib, 6 g Prot, 14 mg Calc. **POINTS** value: *1.*

EXPRESS LANE To get a head start on the recipe, prepare and refrigerate the salsa up to 3 days ahead. You can also cook the shrimp the day before and refrigerate it.

1 large ripe **mango**, peeled, seeded, and finely chopped

½ cup seeded and finely chopped **red bell pepper**

¼ cup finely chopped **red onion**

3 tablespoons chopped **fresh cilantro**

1 tablespoon **fresh lime juice**

¼ teaspoon **salt**

⅛ teaspoon freshly **ground pepper**

4 teaspoons **Cajun seasoning**

36 extra-large **shrimp** (about 1½ pounds), peeled and deveined

3 teaspoons **olive oil**

Tomatoes Stuffed with Italian-Style Tuna

PREP	25 MINUTES
COOK	NONE
SERVES	4

1 Combine the tuna, carrot, onion, fennel, pimiento, parsley, and capers in a medium bowl. Stir in the mayonnaise, oil, and pepper.

2 Cut off the top one-fourth of each tomato, reserving the slices to use as lids. Scoop out and discard the seeds and membranes from the tomatoes. Fill each tomato with ½ cup of the tuna mixture and top with a lid.

PER SERVING (1 stuffed tomato): 165 Cal, 5 g Fat, 1 g Sat Fat, 0 g Trans Fat, 32 mg Chol, 534 mg Sod, 13 g Carb, 3 g Fib, 19 g Prot, 31 mg Calc. **POINTS** value: **3.**

FOOD NOTE To make great bite-size hors d'oeuvres, cut the tuna recipe in half, then hollow out and fill 48 cherry tomatoes with the tuna mixture. This can be done several hours before your party—simply refrigerate the tomatoes until ready to serve.

2 (6-ounce) cans **water-packed solid white tuna** in water, drained and flaked

½ **carrot**, finely chopped

¼ **red onion**, finely chopped

¼ cup finely chopped **fennel**

2 tablespoons drained chopped **pimiento**

2 tablespoons chopped **fresh parsley**

4 teaspoons chopped drained **capers**

⅓ cup **fat-free mayonnaise**

1½ teaspoons **extra-virgin olive oil**

¼ teaspoon freshly **ground pepper**

4 large ripe **tomatoes**

Tomatoes Stuffed with
Italian-Style Tuna

Mussels Dijonnaise

PREP	40 MINUTES PLUS 2 HOURS CHILLING TIME
COOK	ABOUT 15 MINUTES
SERVES	8

1 Combine the mussels, water, shallots, garlic, and thyme in a large saucepan. Cover and bring to a boil over medium heat. Simmer until the mussels open, about 2 minutes. Transfer the mussels with a slotted spoon to a bowl; let cool. Discard any mussels that do not open. Discard the thyme, reserving the broth remaining in the pan.

2 Transfer the solids from the broth with a slotted spoon to a food processor with 2 tablespoons of the broth. Add the egg, oil, vinegar, Dijon and dry mustards, the salt, and pepper; process until smooth. (Refrigerate or freeze the remaining broth for another use.)

3 Remove the mussels from their shells and reserve half the shells for serving. Pour the mustard sauce into a zip-close plastic bag and add the mussels. Squeeze out the air and seal the bag; turn to coat the mussels. Refrigerate, turning the bag occasionally, at least 2 hours or up to 8 hours. Wash and rinse the reserved shells and set aside to dry, or place them, unwashed, in a separate zip-close plastic bag and refrigerate until ready to use.

4 Arrange the shells on a platter or tray, place a mussel with a little sauce into each shell, and sprinkle with the parsley.

PER SERVING (8 mussels): 137 Cal, 6 g Fat, 1 g Sat Fat, 0 g Trans Fat, 58 mg Chol, 453 mg Sod, 6 g Carb, 0 g Fib, 15 g Prot, 40 mg Calc. **POINTS** value: **3.**

PLAY IT SAFE When buying mussels, look for tightly closed shells or shells that close when lightly tapped. Discard any mussels with shells that remain open or that are broken.

2 pounds **mussels**, scrubbed and debearded

¼ cup **water**

2 **shallots**, peeled and chopped

2 **garlic cloves**, finely chopped

2 **fresh thyme sprigs**

1 **hard-cooked large egg**

4 teaspoons **olive oil**

1 tablespoon **white-wine** or **cider vinegar**

1 tablespoon **Dijon mustard**

1 teaspoon **powder mustard**

¼ teaspoon **salt**

Freshly **ground pepper**, to taste

¼ cup minced **fresh flat-leaf parsley**

Grilled Calamari with Arugula and Tomatoes

PREP	25 MINUTES
COOK	ABOUT 5 MINUTES
SERVES	4

1 Spray the grill rack with olive oil nonstick spray; prepare the grill.

2 Combine the vinegar, mustard, ¼ teaspoon of the salt, and ⅛ teaspoon of the pepper in a small bowl. Gradually whisk in the oil until blended.

3 Combine the arugula and tomatoes in a large bowl.

4 Sprinkle the squid with the remaining ½ teaspoon salt and ⅛ teaspoon pepper. Place the squid on the grill rack. Grill until tender but still slightly firm, about 2 minutes on each side. Transfer to a cutting board. Cut each body into 5 rings; add to the arugula and tomatoes. Add the dressing; toss to coat. Serve at once.

PER SERVING (1½ cups): 176 Cal, 9 g Fat, 2 g Sat Fat, 0 g Trans Fat, 240 mg Chol, 584 mg Sod, 7 g Carb, 1 g Fib, 17 g Prot, 73 mg Calc. **POINTS** value: **4.**

FOOD NOTE When you buy calamari (more commonly known as squid), ask your fishmonger for just the bodies and not the tentacles. For best results, pat the squid dry with paper towels before grilling.

4 teaspoons **balsamic vinegar**

2 teaspoons Dijon **mustard**

¾ teaspoon **salt**

¼ teaspoon freshly **ground pepper**

4 teaspoons **extra-virgin olive oil**

4 cups **arugula leaves**

2 **plum tomatoes**, cut into 8 wedges each

1 pound **squid** bodies

Balsamic Tomato-Orange Starter

Balsamic Tomato-Orange Starter

PREP	20 MINUTES
COOK	NONE
SERVES	4

1 Grate 1 teaspoon orange zest from one of the oranges; place in a small bowl and set aside.

2 Remove the peel and the pith from both of the oranges. Trim off ¼ inch from the ends of each orange, then cut each orange into 4 crosswise slices.

3 Trim off ¼ inch from the ends of each tomato, then cut each tomato into 4 crosswise slices.

4 Add the vinegar, parsley, oil, salt, and pepper to the orange zest; mix well.

5 Stack 2 tomato and 2 orange slices alternately on each of 4 salad plates. Drizzle each stack with about 1 tablespoon of the dressing. Serve at once.

PER SERVING (1 stack): 74 Cal, 3 g Fat, 0 g Sat Fat, 0 g Trans Fat, 0 mg Chol, 156 mg Sod, 13 g Carb, 3 g Fib, 2 g Prot, 38 mg Calc.
POINTS value: *1.*

FOOD NOTE If you like, substitute yellow tomatoes for the red and place the stacks on a red or green lettuce leaf.

2 navel oranges

2 ripe tomatoes

2 tablespoons balsamic vinegar

2 tablespoons chopped fresh parsley

2 teaspoons olive oil

¼ teaspoon salt

⅛ teaspoon freshly ground pepper

Marinated Artichokes and Oranges

PREP	15 MINUTES PLUS 4 HOURS CHILLING TIME
COOK	NONE
SERVES	6

2 (14-ounce) cans **artichoke hearts**, drained and quartered

2 medium **oranges**, peeled and cut into segments

1 tablespoon **sherry vinegar**

2 teaspoons **extra-virgin olive oil**

1 teaspoon grated **orange zest**

½ teaspoon **ground cumin**

½ teaspoon **dried oregano**

½ teaspoon **fennel seeds**, lightly crushed

¼ teaspoon **salt**

Combine the artichokes, oranges, vinegar, oil, orange zest, cumin, oregano, fennel seeds, and salt in a medium bowl. Cover and refrigerate at least 4 hours or overnight.

PER SERVING (½ cup): 86 Cal, 2 g Fat, 0 g Sat Fat, 0 g Trans Fat, 0 mg Chol, 389 mg Sod, 17 g Carb, 6 g Fib, 4 g Prot, 66 mg Calc. **POINTS** value: *1.*

HOW WE DID IT When you grate the orange, you want to capture only the zest—the orange skin—and none of the bitter white pith underneath. Grate the peel from the whole orange, then wrap the remaining zest tightly in plastic wrap and freeze for an instant flavor boost. To lightly crush the fennel seeds, place them in a zip-close plastic bag and tap them several times with a rolling pin or can.

Roasted Potato Salad

PREP	15 MINUTES
COOK	35–40 MINUTES
SERVES	6

1 Preheat the oven to 425°F. Spray a roasting pan or shallow baking pan with nonstick spray.

2 Combine the potatoes, oil, and paprika in a medium bowl; toss well to coat. Arrange in a single layer in the roasting pan. Roast, turning occasionally, until the potatoes are lightly browned and tender, 35–40 minutes. Let cool 10 minutes.

3 Meanwhile, combine the mayonnaise, garlic, and coriander in a large bowl. Add the potatoes, bell peppers, celery, onion, salt, and ground pepper; toss well. Serve at once.

PER SERVING (about ¾ cup): 179 Cal, 3 g Fat, 0 g Sat Fat, 0 g Trans Fat, 2 mg Chol, 247 mg Sod, 35 g Carb, 4 g Fib, 4 g Prot, 27 mg Calc.
POINTS value: **3.**

EXPRESS LANE If you're in a hurry, you can use the precut chunks of uncooked red potatoes available in the produce aisle of most supermarkets.

2 pounds **red potatoes**, scrubbed and cut into 1-inch chunks

1 tablespoon **olive oil**

1 teaspoon **paprika**

6 tablespoons **fat-free mayonnaise**

1 **garlic clove**, minced

¼ teaspoon **ground coriander**

½ **red bell pepper**, seeded and chopped

½ **green bell pepper**, seeded and chopped

2 **celery stalks**, chopped

¼ **onion**, chopped

¼ teaspoon **salt**

Freshly **ground pepper**, to taste

Warm White Bean Salad

PREP	30 MINUTES PLUS 1 HOUR STANDING TIME
COOK	40–45 MINUTES
SERVES	6

1 Place the beans in a large pot and cover with water; bring to a boil. Reduce the heat and simmer, covered, 2 minutes. Remove the pot from the heat and let stand 1 hour; drain.

2 Combine the beans and enough fresh water to cover by 4 inches in the same pot. Add the carrot, onion, celery, and bay leaf; bring to a boil. Reduce the heat and simmer until the beans are tender, 40–45 minutes. Drain and discard the vegetables and bay leaf. Let the beans cool 10 minutes; transfer to a large serving bowl.

3 Add the egg whites, tomatoes, bell pepper, red onion, olives, parsley, vinegar, oil, salt, and pepper. Toss gently and serve at once.

PER SERVING (1 cup): 118 Cal, 6 g Fat, 1 g Sat Fat, 0 g Trans Fat, 0 mg Chol, 542 mg Sod, 13 g Carb, 3 g Fib, 5 g Prot, 28 mg Calc.
POINTS value: **2.**

EXPRESS LANE While you're at it, why not make a double batch of beans, up to Step 2, and use the extra in a soup or chili for a speedy meal later in the week? They'll keep up to 4 days in the refrigerator.

1 cup **dried cannellini (white kidney) beans**, picked over, rinsed, and drained

1 **carrot**, cut into 2-inch pieces

1 **onion**, quartered

1 **celery stalk**, cut into 2-inch pieces

1 **bay leaf**

2 **hard-cooked egg whites**, chopped

2 **tomatoes**, seeded and chopped

1 **green bell pepper**, seeded and chopped

1 small **red onion**, finely chopped

12 large **green pimiento-stuffed olives**, chopped

¼ cup chopped **fresh parsley**

2 tablespoons **sherry vinegar**

2 tablespoons **extra-virgin olive oil**

¾ teaspoon **salt**

Freshly **ground pepper**, to taste

Warm White Bean Salad

Green-and-Yellow Salad with Microwave Onion Vinaigrette

PREP	40 MINUTES
COOK	ABOUT 30 MINUTES
SERVES	4

☑

1 Combine the onion and 1 teaspoon of the oil in a microwavable 9-inch pie dish. Microwave on High, stirring once halfway through cooking, until the onion is tender, about 5 minutes. Stir in the broth. Microwave until the broth is hot, 1 minute. Transfer to a small bowl; stir in remaining 1½ teaspoons oil, the lemon zest, lemon juice, garlic, and salt. Cover and refrigerate until ready to use, up to 2 days.

2 Fill a 2-quart saucepan with water and squeeze one lemon half into it. Working one at a time, cut a thin slice from the stem end of each artichoke. Peel the stems with a vegetable peeler and rub with the other lemon half. Remove and discard tough outer leaves of artichokes until the tender yellow leaves are exposed, then drop into the lemon water.

3 Bring the artichokes and lemon water to a boil; reduce the heat and simmer until a knife can pierce the base of the artichoke with just a hint of resistance, about 9 minutes. Drain the artichokes in a colander under cool running water until they reach room temperature. Cut them in half lengthwise and, with a small knife, remove the fuzzy choke and prickly purple leaves. Transfer the artichokes to a serving bowl and toss with the dressing, bell peppers, and edamame.

PER SERVING (generous 1 cup): 144 Cal, 4 g Fat, 0 g Sat Fat, 0 mg Trans Fat, 0 mg Chol, 400 mg Sod, 21 g Carb, 9 g Fib, 8 g Prot, 82 mg Calc. **POINTS** value: **2.**

- 1 medium **red onion**, cut into 1-inch chunks
- 2½ teaspoons **extra-virgin olive oil**
- ¼ cup **reduced-sodium chicken broth**
- ½ teaspoon grated **lemon zest**
- 1 tablespoon **fresh lemon juice**
- 1 small **garlic clove**, minced
- ½ teaspoon **salt**
- 1 **lemon**, halved
- 6 baby **artichokes**
- 2 large **yellow bell peppers**, seeded and cut into chunks
- 1 cup shelled fresh or frozen and **thawed edamame** (green soybeans)

EXPRESS LANE *Edamame* (eh-dah-MAH-meh) is the Japanese name for good-for-you green soybeans. Now conveniently available shelled and frozen in larger supermarkets or natural foods stores, *edamame* resemble baby lima beans in both their appearance and use.

Broccoli and Roasted Peppers with Chickpeas

PREP	15 MINUTES
COOK	ABOUT 15 MINUTES
SERVES	4

1 Bring a large pot of water to a boil. Add the broccoli and cook until crisp-tender, about 3 minutes. Drain the broccoli in a colander, rinse under cold water. Transfer the broccoli to paper towels; drain.

2 Meanwhile, mash the garlic, salt, and lemon zest to a paste with the side of a heavy knife. Transfer to a serving bowl; whisk in the lemon juice, oil, and ground pepper. Stir in the roasted peppers and chickpeas.

3 Just before serving, stir the broccoli into the roasted pepper mixture.

PER SERVING (1½ cups): 127 Cal, 6 g Fat, 1 g Sat Fat, 0 g Trans Fat, 0 mg Chol, 369 mg Sod, 15 g Carb, 5 g Fib, 5 g Prot, 57 mg Calc. **POINTS** value: **2.**

EXPRESS LANE For even less prep, take advantage of packaged broccoli florets available in the produce section of the supermarket.

4 cups **broccoli florets**

1 **garlic clove**, chopped

¼ teaspoon **salt**

¼ teaspoon grated **lemon zest**

3 tablespoons **fresh lemon juice**

1½ tablespoons **sunflower** or **canola oil**

⅛ teaspoon freshly **ground pepper**

2 jarred **roasted yellow** or **red bell peppers**, drained, patted dry, and cut into long thin strips

1 cup canned **chickpeas**, rinsed and drained

Roasted Bell Peppers and
Radicchio with Rosemary

Roasted Bell Peppers and Radicchio with Rosemary

PREP	20 MINUTES
COOK	ABOUT 10 MINUTES
SERVES	4

1 Preheat the oven to 500°F. Spray a large nonstick baking pan with nonstick spray.

2 Combine the bell peppers, radicchio, onion, rosemary, oil, salt, and ground pepper in a large bowl; toss to coat. Arrange the vegetables on the baking pan in a single layer. Roast until lightly browned, about 6 minutes on each side. Serve hot, warm, or at room temperature.

PER SERVING (1 cup): 61 Cal, 4 g Fat, 1 g Sat Fat, 0 g Trans Fat, 0 mg Chol, 443 mg Sod, 7 g Carb, 2 g Fib, 1 g Prot, 17 mg Calc.
POINTS value: *1.*

EXPRESS LANE When prepping the radicchio for roasting, leave the core attached to each wedge to help hold the wedges intact.

1 **red bell pepper**, seeded and cut into eighths

1 **yellow bell pepper**, seeded and cut into eighths

1 head **radicchio**, cut into 8 wedges

1 medium **red onion**, cut into eighths

1½ tablespoons chopped **fresh rosemary**, or 1½ teaspoons dried, crumbled

1 tablespoon **olive oil**

¾ teaspoon **salt**

Freshly **ground pepper**, to taste

CHAPTER 2

Time for Soup

Beef, Rice, and Root Vegetable Soup

☑

PREP	25 MINUTES
COOK	35 MINUTES
SERVES	6

1 Heat the oil in a Dutch oven over medium heat. Add one third of the beef and cook, stirring occasionally, until browned, about 3 minutes. Transfer the beef to a plate with a slotted spoon. Repeat with remaining beef.

2 Add the carrots, parsnips, turnips, onion, bay leaves, caraway seeds, and thyme to the Dutch oven. Cook, stirring constantly, until the vegetables are slightly softened, about 3 minutes. Stir in the beef with any accumulated juices, the broth, water, tomato paste, salt, and pepper; bring to a boil. Reduce the heat and simmer until the beef and vegetables are tender, about 20 minutes. Remove the bay leaves; stir in the spinach and brown rice.

PER SERVING (about 1⅓ cups): 267 Cal, 5 g Fat, 1 g Sat Fat, 0 g Trans Fat, 29 mg Chol, 578 mg Sod, 38 g Carb, 7 g Fib, 19 g Prot, 78 mg Calc. **POINTS** value: **5.**

GOOD IDEA This is a great way to use leftover take-out brown rice. Or if you wish to cook the rice yourself, bring 1¾ cups water to a boil in a medium saucepan. Add ¾ cup brown rice and ¼ teaspoon salt; return to a boil. Reduce the heat and simmer, covered, until the rice is tender and the liquid is absorbed, about 45 minutes. Remove the saucepan from the heat; let stand, covered, 10 minutes. Fluff with a fork.

1 tablespoon **canola oil**

¾ pound **top round steak**, trimmed and cut into ½-inch dice

4 **carrots**, chopped

3 **parsnips**, peeled and chopped

2 cups peeled and chopped **turnips**

1 large **onion**, thinly sliced

2 **bay leaves**

¾ teaspoon **caraway seeds**, crushed

½ teaspoon **dried thyme**, crumbled

4 cups reduced-sodium **beef broth**

3 cups **water**

2 tablespoons **tomato paste**

½ teaspoon **salt**

¼ teaspoon freshly **ground pepper**

2 cups packed finely shredded **fresh spinach leaves**

1½ cups cooked **brown rice**

Beef, Rice, and Root
Vegetable Soup

Asian Pork and Noodle Soup

PREP	30 MINUTES
COOK	20 MINUTES
SERVES	4

1 Bring the broth, scallions, ginger, and soy sauce to a boil in a large pot or Dutch oven. Reduce the heat and simmer until the scallions are tender, about 5 minutes. Add the sliced bok choy stalks, return to a simmer, and cook until the bok choy is barely tender, about 7 minutes.

2 Stir in the spaghetti, pork, bok choy leaves, turnips, and carrots; simmer just until the leaves are wilted, about 2 minutes.

PER SERVING (2 cups): 230 Cal, 3 g Fat, 1 g Sat Fat, 0 g Trans Fat, 140 mg Chol, 1,141 mg Sod, 29 g Carb, 7 g Fib, 23 g Prot, 98 mg Calc. *POINTS* value: *4.*

GOOD IDEA If you can't find bok choy in your supermarket, substitute chopped napa cabbage—no need to separate the stems and leaves; just reduce the cooking time to 2 minutes. For a touch of heat, add a pinch of crushed red pepper or hot pepper sauce as the soup simmers.

1 (48-ounce) can **reduced-sodium chicken broth**

1 small bunch **scallions**, chopped

1 tablespoon minced peeled **fresh ginger**

1 tablespoon **reduced-sodium soy sauce**

3 cups thinly sliced **bok choy**, stalks and leaves separated

2 cups cooked **whole-wheat spaghetti**

6 ounces **lean cooked pork**, cut into matchstick-size strips

1 cup diced **cooked turnips**

1 cup diced **cooked carrots**

Slow-Cooker Veal and Bean Soup

☑

PREP	15 MINUTES PLUS 1 HOUR STANDING TIME
COOK	3½–4 HOURS
SERVES	6

1 Presoak the beans according to package directions; drain in a colander.

2 Heat 2 teaspoons of the oil in a large nonstick skillet over medium heat. Add the onion, carrots, and fennel; cook, stirring occasionally, until the vegetables are almost tender, about 4 minutes. Transfer the vegetables to a 5- or 6-quart slow cooker.

3 Heat the remaining 2 teaspoons oil in the same skillet over medium-high heat. Add the veal and garlic; cook, stirring occasionally, until browned, about 5 minutes. Transfer to the slow cooker.

4 Stir half of the broth into the skillet; bring to a boil. Cook, stirring constantly to scrape the browned bits from the bottom of the skillet. Pour the broth mixture and the remaining broth over the veal. Add the beans, sage, rosemary, and crushed red pepper; mix well. Cover and cook until the veal and beans are tender, 3½–4 hours on high or 7–8 hours on low.

PER SERVING (about 1⅓ cups): 269 Cal, 7 g Fat, 1 g Sat Fat, 1 g Trans Fat, 39 mg Chol, 373 mg Sod, 32 g Carb, 12 g Fib, 21 g Prot, 111 mg Calc. *POINTS* value: *5.*

EXPRESS LANE If you want to speed things up and skip the slow cooking, prepare the recipe as directed except use a large saucepan instead of a skillet. Transfer the sautéed vegetables to a bowl, then brown the veal. Return the vegetables to the pan and add the remaining ingredients; bring to a boil. Reduce the heat and simmer, covered, until the veal is very tender, 65 to 75 minutes.

½ pound **dried cannellini** (white kidney) **beans**, picked over, rinsed, and drained

4 teaspoons **olive oil**

1 **onion**, finely chopped

2 **carrots**, finely chopped

1 medium **fennel bulb**, finely chopped

¾ pound **boneless veal loin**, trimmed and cut into 1-inch chunks

2 large **garlic cloves**, minced

3 cups **reduced-sodium chicken broth**

1 tablespoon chopped **fresh sage**, or 1 teaspoon dried

½ teaspoon chopped **fresh rosemary**, or ¼ teaspoon dried

¼ teaspoon crushed **red pepper**

Smoked Chicken, Tea,
and Noodle Soup

Smoked Chicken, Tea, and Noodle Soup

PREP	15 MINUTES
COOK	ABOUT 25 MINUTES
SERVES	4

1 Cook the spaghetti according to package directions; drain in a colander.

2 Meanwhile, bring the broth and water to a simmer in a soup pot or Dutch oven. Add the carrots, mushrooms, ginger, and garlic; reduce the heat and simmer 2 minutes. Add the tea bag; remove the pot from the heat and let tea steep about 2 minutes. Remove the tea bag and ginger.

3 Stir the spaghetti, chicken, watercress, and scallions into the Dutch oven; simmer just until heated through, about 2 minutes. Serve at once.

PER SERVING (1¼cups): 205 Cal, 3 g Fat, 0 g Sat Fat, 0 g Trans Fat, 30 mg Chol, 1,360 mg Sod, 30 g Carb, 5 g Fib, 19 g Prot, 37 mg Calc. *POINTS* value: *4.*

GOOD IDEA Use Earl Grey tea, delicately scented with the Mediterranean citrus fruit bergamot, for the best flavor.

☑

¼ pound **whole-wheat spaghetti**

1 (32-ounce) container **reduced-sodium chicken broth**

1 cup **water**

2 **carrots**, halved lengthwise and thinly sliced

¼ pound **fresh shiitake** or **cremini mushrooms**, sliced

2 quarter-size slices unpeeled **fresh ginger**

1 **garlic clove**, minced

1 **black tea bag**

½ pound boneless **smoked chicken** or **turkey breast**, cut into matchstick-size strips

⅔ cup packed **watercress leaves**

3 **scallions**, sliced

Chicken Noodle Soup

PREP	20 MINUTES
COOK	1 HOUR
SERVES	4

1 Spray a nonstick Dutch oven with canola nonstick spray and set over medium heat. Add the onions, carrots, parsnip, and celery; cook, stirring occasionally, until slightly softened, about 10 minutes.

2 Stir in the broth, chicken, bay leaf, and dill; bring to a boil. Reduce the heat and simmer, covered, about 30 minutes. Add the linguine and return to a simmer. Cook, partially covered, until the vegetables and linguine are tender and the chicken is cooked through, about 15 minutes. Discard the bay leaf. Stir in the salt and pepper.

PER SERVING (2 cups): 362 Cal, 9 g Fat, 2 g Sat Fat, 0 g Trans Fat, 76 mg Chol, 1,170 mg Sod, 41 g Carb, 8 g Fib, 31 g Prot, 68 mg Calc. **POINTS** value: **7**.

GOOD IDEA If you're looking for an even richer tasting soup, use bone-in skinless chicken thighs. Prepare the recipe as directed except leave the thighs whole and increase the cooking time to about 1 hour before adding the linguine. Remove the chicken from the soup; let cool. Pull the chicken from the bones, cut into 1-inch pieces, and return to the soup.

2 **onions**, chopped

2 **carrots**, chopped

1 **parsnip**, chopped

1 **celery stalk**, chopped

5 cups **reduced-sodium chicken broth**

1 pound **skinless boneless chicken thighs**, cut into 1-inch pieces

1 **bay leaf**

2 tablespoons chopped **fresh dill**

4 ounces **whole-wheat linguine**, broken into thirds

½ teaspoon **salt**

¼ teaspoon freshly **ground pepper**

Easiest Tortilla Chicken Soup

PREP	10 MINUTES
COOK	ABOUT 10 MINUTES
SERVES	4

1 Heat the oil in a large nonstick saucepan over medium-high heat. Add the onion, bell pepper, and garlic; cook, stirring frequently, until softened and lightly browned, about 5 minutes.

2 Add the broth, tomatoes, corn, and chili seasoning mix; bring to a boil over high heat. Add the chicken and cilantro. Reduce the heat and simmer until heated through, about 2 minutes. Serve with the tortilla chips.

PER SERVING (1½ cups soup and 2 tortilla chips): 230 Cal, 4 g Fat, 1 g Sat Fat, 0 g Trans Fat, 43 mg Chol, 801 mg Sod, 29 g Carb, 4 g Fib, 22 g Prot, 66 mg Calc. **POINTS** value: **4.**

EXPRESS LANE To save time chopping, you can use 1 cup each of frozen chopped onions and frozen chopped green bell peppers instead of the fresh onion and bell pepper.

1 teaspoon **canola oil**

1 **onion**, chopped

1 **green bell pepper**, seeded and chopped

2 **garlic cloves**, minced

3 cups **reduced-sodium chicken broth**

1 (14½-ounce) **can diced tomatoes with mild green chiles**

1 (10-ounce) package **frozen corn kernels**, thawed

1 teaspoon **chili seasoning mix**

1½ cups chopped **cooked chicken breast**

¼ cup coarsely chopped **fresh cilantro** or **parsley**

8 large **baked tortilla chips**, coarsely broken up

Shrimp and Cabbage Chowder

PREP	20 MINUTES
COOK	ABOUT 25 MINUTES
SERVES	4

1 Heat the oil in a soup pot or Dutch oven over medium-high heat. Add the garlic and cook, stirring constantly, just until fragrant, about 20 seconds. Add the broth, cabbage, beans, and crushed red pepper; bring to a boil. Reduce the heat and simmer, covered, until the cabbage is very tender, about 12 minutes.

2 Stir in the shrimp, tomatoes, and basil; cook, uncovered, stirring occasionally, until the shrimp is just opaque in the center, 2-3 minutes. Serve at once.

PER SERVING (1¾ cups): 251 Cal, 5 g Fat, 1 g Sat Fat, 0 g Trans Fat, 168 mg Chol, 1,024 mg Sod, 25 g Carb, 8 g Fib, 29 g Prot, 121 mg Calc. **POINTS** value: **5.**

GOOD IDEA Savoy cabbage, with its tender sweet leaves, is best in this recipe, but regular green cabbage can certainly be substituted. Whatever variety you choose, be sure it is very tender before adding the shrimp.

☑

1 tablespoon **olive oil**

3 large **garlic cloves,** finely chopped

2 (14½-ounce) cans **reduced-sodium chicken broth**

1 small head **Savoy cabbage** (1 pound), thinly sliced

1 (15-ounce) can **navy** or other **white beans,** rinsed and drained

¼ teaspoon **crushed red pepper** or freshly **ground pepper**

1 pound large **shrimp,** peeled and deveined

2 **plum tomatoes,** diced

½ cup packed **fresh basil** leaves, thinly sliced

Manhattan Clam Chowder

PREP	20 MINUTES
COOK	ABOUT 30 MINUTES
SERVES	4

1 Heat the oil in a large nonstick saucepan over medium-high heat. Add the onion and cook, stirring occasionally, until softened, about 4 minutes. Add the potato, zucchini, celery, and carrot; cook, stirring occasionally, until the onion is golden, 3–5 minutes.

2 Add the tomatoes, clam juice, hot water, thyme, oregano, and pepper to the saucepan; bring to a boil. Reduce the heat and simmer, partially covered, until the vegetables are tender, about 15 minutes. Add the clams; simmer just until heated through, 1–2 minutes (do not boil, or the clams will toughen).

PER SERVING (1½ cups): 127 Cal, 3 g Fat, 0 g Sat Fat, 0 g Trans Fat, 16 mg Chol, 209 mg Sod, 18 g Carb, 4 g Fib, 8 g Prot, 81 mg Calc. *POINTS* value: *2.*

GOOD IDEA For a pleasant crunch, sprinkle ¼ cup oyster crackers over each serving (remember to deduct them from your weekly *POINTS* Allowance—¼ cup will increase the *POINTS* value by 1).

2 teaspoons **olive oil**

1 **onion**, finely chopped

1 **potato**, peeled and finely chopped

1 small (8-ounce) **zucchini**, finely chopped

1 **celery stalk**, finely chopped

1 **carrot**, finely chopped

1 (14-ounce) can **Italian-style diced tomatoes** (no salt added)

1 (8-ounce) bottle **clam juice**

1½ cups hot **water**

1½ teaspoons fresh **thyme leaves**, or ½ teaspoon dried

1½ teaspoons **fresh oregano** or **marjoram leaves**, or ½ teaspoon dried

Freshly **ground pepper**, to taste

1 (6½-ounce) can chopped **clams** (do not drain)

Chilled Tomato and Shrimp Soup

PREP	15 MINUTES PLUS 1 HOUR CHILLING TIME
COOK	25 MINUTES
SERVES	6

1 Combine the tomatoes, broth, onion, tomato paste, garlic, salt, and pepper in a Dutch oven; bring to a boil. Reduce the heat and simmer, covered, until the onion is tender, about 20 minutes. Remove the Dutch oven from the heat and let cool slightly.

2 Pour the soup in 2 batches into a blender or food processor and puree. Transfer to a large bowl; stir in the buttermilk. Cover and refrigerate until well chilled, at least 1 hour. Just before serving, stir in the shrimp, cucumber, dill, and chives.

PER SERVING (1⅓ cups): 133 Cal, 1 g Fat, 0 g Sat Fat, 0 g Trans Fat, 95 mg Chol, 604 mg Sod, 11 g Carb, 2 g Fib, 20 g Prot, 95 mg Calc. *POINTS* value: *2.*

GOOD IDEA This is a great do-ahead soup. Prepare as directed except do not stir in the shrimp, cucumber, dill, and chives. Transfer to an airtight container and refrigerate up to 4 days. Stir in the remaining ingredients when ready to serve.

3 large ripe **tomatoes**, coarsely chopped

2 cups **reduced-sodium chicken broth**

1 large **onion**, coarsely chopped

2 tablespoons **tomato paste**

2 **garlic cloves**, coarsely chopped

½ teaspoon **salt**

¼ teaspoon freshly **ground pepper**

1 cup **fat-free buttermilk**

1 pound frozen cooked **shrimp**, thawed and cut into chunks

½ **seedless cucumber**, diced

¼ cup chopped **fresh dill**

¼ cup minced **fresh chives**

Wild Mushroom and Rice Soup

PREP	10 MINUTES
COOK	ABOUT 30 MINUTES
SERVES	4

1 Heat the oil in a nonstick Dutch oven over medium-high heat. Add the poblanos and onion; cook, stirring occasionally, until softened, about 4 minutes. Add the mushrooms and cook, stirring occasionally, until the mushrooms are tender, about 5 minutes.

2 Add the tomatoes, broth, water, chili powder, and salt; bring to a boil. Reduce the heat and simmer, covered, until the flavors are blended, about 5 minutes. Add the rice; simmer, covered, until tender, about 10 minutes. Remove the Dutch oven from the heat; stir in the cilantro.

PER SERVING (1½ cups): 158 Cal, 3 g Fat, 0 g Sat Fat, 0 g Trans Fat, 0 mg Chol, 530 mg Sod, 29 g Carb, 6 g Fib, 7 g Prot, 46 mg Calc. **POINTS** value: **3**.

GOOD IDEA You can prepare the soup and refrigerate it up to 3 days, but you may need to stir in a bit of water when ready to reheat (the rice tends to absorb a good amount of the liquid).

1 teaspoon **olive oil**

2 **poblano peppers**, seeded and chopped (wear gloves to prevent irritation)

1 **onion**, chopped

3 (4-ounce) packages assorted sliced **fresh wild mushrooms** (such as oyster, baby bella, and shiitake)

1 (14½-ounce) **can diced tomatoes** in juice

1½ cups **reduced-sodium chicken broth**

1 cup **water**

2 teaspoons **chili powder**

¼ teaspoon **salt**

½ cup **quick-cooking brown rice**

⅓ cup chopped **fresh cilantro**

Fresh Cream of Tomato Soup

PREP	15 MINUTES PLUS 20 MINUTES COOLING TIME
COOK	ABOUT 15 MINUTES
SERVES	4

1 Heat the oil a large nonstick saucepan over medium heat. Add the onions and cook, stirring occasionally, until softened, about 5 minutes. Stir in the tomatoes, broth, garlic, thyme, and basil (if using dried). Simmer, covered, until the vegetables are tender, about 5 minutes. Cool slightly; transfer to a blender and puree.

2 Return the mixture to the saucepan. Whisk the milk and tomato paste in a small bowl; stir into the soup. Add the basil, salt, and pepper; cook, stirring occasionally, until just heated through (do not boil).

PER SERVING (1¼ cups): 198 Cal, 6 g Fat, 1 g Sat Fat, 0 g Trans Fat, 4 mg Chol, 861 mg Sod, 29 g Carb, 4 g Fib, 11 g Prot, 263 mg Calc
POINTS value: **4.**

HOW WE DID IT To peel the tomatoes, drop them into a large pot of boiling water and remove after 10 seconds with a slotted spoon. Immediately drop the tomatoes into a bowl of ice water to stop the cooking. The skins should be loosened just enough to peel.

4 teaspoons **olive oil**

2 **onions**, finely chopped

4 large ripe **tomatoes**, peeled and coarsely chopped

1 cup **vegetable broth**

3 **garlic cloves**, minced

4 teaspoons chopped **fresh thyme**, or 1 teaspoon dried

4 teaspoons finely chopped **fresh basil**, or 1 teaspoon dried

3 cups **fat-free milk**

¼ cup **tomato paste**

1 teaspoon **salt**

Freshly **ground pepper**, to taste

Broiled Cheese, Bread, and Bean Soup

Broiled Cheese, Bread, and Bean Soup

PREP	5 MINUTES
COOK	ABOUT 15 MINUTES
SERVES	4

1 Heat the oil in an ovenproof Dutch oven over medium-high heat. Add the onion and garlic; cook, stirring frequently, until softened, about 3 minutes. Add the broth, tomatoes, spinach, and pepper; bring to a boil over high heat, stirring occasionally. Reduce the heat and simmer, covered, until the flavors are blended, about 2 minutes. Stir in the beans and cook until hot, about 3 minutes.

2 Meanwhile, preheat the broiler. Stir the bread chunks into the soup; sprinkle with the cheese. Stand the Dutch oven on the oven rack and broil 4 inches from the heat until the cheese and bread are lightly browned, 1–2 minutes.

PER SERVING (1¾ cups): 401 Cal, 8 g Fat, 3 g Sat Fat, 0 g Trans Fat, 12 mg Chol, 1114 mg Sod, 62 g Carb, 14 g Fib, 23 g Prot, 332 mg Calc. **POINTS** value: **8.**

DEFINITION *Manchego* (mahn-CHAY-goh) cheese, the most popular sheep's milk cheese in Spain, is full of flavor and melts beautifully. If you can't find it in your market, substitute Monterey Jack or cheddar cheese.

- 2 teaspoons **extra-virgin olive oil**
- 1 **onion**, chopped
- 3 **garlic cloves**, minced
- 4 cups **reduced-sodium vegetable broth**
- 1 (14½-ounce) can diced **tomatoes with Italian herbs**
- 1 (10-ounce) package frozen chopped **spinach**, thawed and squeezed dry
- ¼ teaspoon freshly **ground pepper**
- 2 (15½-ounce) cans **cannellini** (white kidney) **beans**, rinsed and drained
- 4 ounces **Italian bread**, cut into chunks
- ½ cup shredded **manchego cheese**

Creamy Cannellini Bean Soup

PREP	15 MINUTES
COOK	ABOUT 15 MINUTES
SERVES	4

1 Puree the broth and beans in batches in a blender; set aside in a large bowl.

2 Heat the oil in a large nonstick saucepan over medium heat. Add the carrots, onion, bell pepper, and garlic; cook, stirring occasionally, until crisp-tender, about 5 minutes. Add the cumin and cook, stirring, until just fragrant, about 30 seconds. Stir in the bean mixture, the lemon juice, thyme, salt, and pepper. Bring to a boil; reduce the heat and simmer, covered, until the carrots are completely tender, about 5 minutes. Sprinkle with the parsley.

PER SERVING (1¼ cups): 271 Cal, 7 g Fat, 1 g Sat Fat, 0 g Trans Fat, 0 mg Chol, 1,114 mg Sod, 39 g Carb, 10 g Fib, 14 g Prot, 101 mg Calc. **POINTS** value: **5.**

ZAP IT Leftovers can be refrigerated in an airtight container up to 5 days. To reheat one serving, thin with a little water, and microwave on Medium until just heated through, 1 to 1½ minutes.

- 5 cups **reduced-sodium chicken broth**
- 3 cups rinsed drained canned **cannellini** (white kidney) **beans**
- 1 tablespoon **olive oil**
- 12 **baby carrots**, thinly sliced
- 1 **onion**, finely chopped
- 1 **red bell pepper**, seeded and finely chopped
- 3 **garlic cloves**, minced
- 1 teaspoon **ground cumin**
- ¼ cup **fresh lemon juice**
- 1 teaspoon **dried thyme**
- ⅛ teaspoon **salt**
- Freshly **ground pepper**, to taste
- 2 tablespoons finely chopped **fresh flat-leaf parsley**

Chickpea and Parsley Soup

PREP	5 MINUTES
COOK	ABOUT 15 MINUTES
SERVES	4

1 Puree the chickpeas, ½ cup of the broth, and the parsley in a food processor.

2 Heat the oil in a large nonstick saucepan over medium-high heat. Add the shallot and cook, stirring frequently, until golden, about 2 minutes. Add the cognac, if using, and cook 30 seconds. Add the remaining 2½ cups broth and the chickpea mixture; bring to a boil over high heat, stirring occasionally. Reduce the heat and simmer, uncovered, stirring occasionally, about 2 minutes.

3 Add the half-and-half and cheese; cook over low heat just until the mixture comes to a simmer. Serve with the pepper.

PER SERVING (1¼ cups): 337 Cal, 8 g Fat, 2 g Sat Fat, 0 g Trans Fat, 8 mg Chol, 581 mg Sod, 50 g Carb, 10 g Fib, 18 g Prot, 246 mg Calc. **POINTS** value: **7.**

FOOD NOTE If you like a little texture in your soup, process the chickpeas and parsley in the food processor until just chunky-smooth.

2 (15½-ounce) cans **chickpeas**, rinsed and drained

3 cups **vegetable broth**

2 cups lightly packed **flat-leaf parsley leaves** and thin stems

2 teaspoons **extra-virgin olive oil**

1 **shallot**, finely chopped

1–2 tablespoons **cognac** (optional)

½ cup **fat-free half-and-half**

¼ cup shredded **Parmesan cheese**

Freshly **ground pepper**

Fresh Corn Chowder

PREP	20 MINUTES
COOK	ABOUT 20 MINUTES
SERVES	4

1 Heat the oil in a large nonstick saucepan over medium heat. Add the bell peppers and shallots; cook, stirring occasionally, until tender, about 5 minutes. Add the curry powder and cook, stirring constantly, until just fragrant, about 30 seconds.

2 Stir in the corn, potatoes, broth, salt, and pepper; bring to a boil. Reduce the heat and simmer, covered, until the vegetables are tender, about 10 minutes.

3 Transfer ½ cup of the vegetable mixture to a blender; add the milk and puree until nearly smooth. Return to the saucepan and cook over medium heat, stirring, until just heated through. Sprinkle with the paprika just before serving.

PER SERVING (1½ cups): 284 Cal, 6 g Fat, 1 g Sat Fat, 0 g Trans Fat, 3 mg Chol, 450 mg Sod, 52 g Carb, 5 g Fib, 12 g Prot, 260 mg Calc.
POINTS value: **5.**

GOOD IDEA If you love curry, try increasing the amount of curry powder, depending on its intensity, up to 2 teaspoons.

4 teaspoons **canola oil**

½ cup seeded and finely chopped **green bell pepper**

½ cup seeded and finely chopped **red bell pepper**

½ cup minced **shallots**

1 teaspoon **curry powder**

3 cups fresh **corn kernels** (from 6 ears)

¾ pound **red potatoes**, peeled and cut into ¼-inch cubes

1 cup **vegetable broth**

½ teaspoon **salt**

Freshly **ground pepper**, to taste

3 cups **fat-free milk**

⅛ teaspoon **paprika**

Fresh Corn Chowder

Pumpkin Soup with Sour Cream and Lime

PREP	5 MINUTES
COOK	COOK TIME: ABOUT 15 MINUTES
SERVES	4

1 Heat the oil in a large nonstick saucepan over medium-high heat. Add the onion, ginger, and nutmeg; cook, stirring frequently, until softened and fragrant, about 3 minutes.

2 Transfer the mixture to a food processor. Add the apple and ½ cup of the broth; puree.

3 Return the mixture to the saucepan and add the remaining 2½ cups broth, the pumpkin, salt, and pepper. Bring the mixture to a boil over high heat, stirring occasionally. Reduce the heat and simmer, about 2 minutes.

4 Combine the sour cream and lime juice in a small bowl. Divide the soup among 4 bowls. Swirl a tablespoon of the sour cream mixture into each bowl and serve at once.

PER SERVING (generous 1 cup soup and 1 tablespoon sour cream mixture): 117 Cal, 4 g Fat, 0 g Sat Fat, 0 g Trans Fat, 1 mg Chol, 519 mg Sod, 21 g Carb, 4 g Fib, 2 g Prot, 60 mg Calc.
POINTS value: *2.*

GOOD IDEA If you have time, grated lime zest makes a nice garnish to this soup. Be sure to grate the lime before squeezing out the juice.

1 tablespoon **canola oil**

1 **onion**, chopped

½ teaspoon **ground ginger**

⅛ teaspoon **ground nutmeg**

1 **Granny Smith apple**, peeled, cored, and coarsely chopped

3 cups **vegetable broth**

1 (15-ounce) can **pumpkin puree**

½ teaspoon **salt**

¼ teaspoon freshly **ground pepper**

¼ cup **fat-free sour cream**

1 teaspoon **fresh lime juice**

Vichyssoise with Olive-Egg Garnish

PREP	10 MINUTES PLUS 3 HOURS CHILLING TIME
COOK	20 MINUTES
SERVES	4

4 cups **reduced-sodium vegetable broth**

4 small **Yukon Gold potatoes**, peeled and cut into ½-inch cubes

½ cup coarsely chopped **shallots**

1 cup **fat-free milk**

½ teaspoon **salt**

Pinch **ground white pepper**

4 **hard-cooked large eggs**

¼ cup finely chopped **black olives**

¼ cup finely chopped **fresh flat-leaf parsley**

1 Bring the broth, potatoes, and shallots to a boil in a medium saucepan. Reduce the heat and simmer, covered, until the potatoes are tender, about 15 minutes. Let cool slightly, then transfer to a blender and puree in batches until just smooth (do not over process).

2 Stir in the milk, salt, and white pepper; transfer to a bowl. Cover and refrigerate until chilled, at least 3 hours.

3 Meanwhile, finely crumble the eggs with a fork in a small bowl. Stir in the olives and parsley. Cover and refrigerate until ready to use. Sprinkle over the soup just before serving.

PER SERVING (1¼ cups): 220 Cal, 6 g Fat, 2 g Sat Fat, 0 g Trans Fat, 214 Chol, 719 mg Sod, 30 g Carb, 3 g Fib, 11 g Prot, 168 mg Calc. *POINTS* value: *4.*

HOW WE DID IT After hard-cooking the eggs, place them in cold water immediately to stop the cooking. This will prevent a dark gray-green surface from forming around the yolks. Quick cooling also causes the eggs to contract in its shell, making them easy to peel. Hard-cooked eggs will keep up to 1 week in the refrigerator.

CHAPTER 3

Our Best Salads

Fruity Chicken Salad

Fruity Chicken Salad

PREP	20 MINUTES
COOK	NONE
SERVES	2

1 Combine the grapes, chicken, onion, bell pepper, and mayonnaise in a small bowl.

2 Spoon half the salad in the hollowed-out center of each cantaloupe half.

PER SERVING (½ cantaloupe with about 1½ cups salad): 251 Cal, 3 g Fat, 1 g Sat Fat, 0 g Trans Fat, 37 mg Chol, 135 mg Sod, 43 g Carb, 4 g Fib, 17 g Prot, 54 mg Calc. *POINTS* value: *4.*

GOOD IDEA Jazz up the salad with a sprinkling of freshly ground black pepper if you like.

40 small **seedless green grapes**, halved

¾ cup diced **cooked chicken breast**

½ cup chopped **onion**

½ cup seeded and chopped **green bell pepper**

4 teaspoons **fat-free mayonnaise**

1 small **cantaloupe**, halved and seeded

Zesty Roast Beef Salad

PREP	15 MINUTES
COOK	NONE
SERVES	4

1 Cut the beef slices into ¼-inch-thick strips.

2 Combine the mayonnaise, sour cream, horseradish, salt, and pepper in a large bowl. Add the lettuce and the beef; toss until well coated. Serve at once.

PER SERVING (about 2 cups): 94 Cal, 2 g Fat, 1 g Sat Fat, 0 g Trans Fat, 29 mg Chol, 807 mg Sod, 6 g Carb, 1 g Fib, 13 g Prot, 55 mg Calc. **POINTS** value: **2.**

GOOD IDEA If you like, serve the salad in edible bread bowls. Pull out the soft bread insides of 4 high-fiber rolls, halved, to make hollowed-out bread shells. Tear the bread into small pieces. Prepare the salad as directed; stir in the bread pieces. Divide the salad into the roll halves; serve at once. Remember to deduct the bread from your **weekly POINTS Allowance** (a 2-ounce high-fiber roll will increase the **POINTS** value by 2).

½ pound thinly sliced **lean roast beef**

2 tablespoons **fat-free mayonnaise**

2 tablespoons **fat-free sour cream**

2 teaspoons prepared **horseradish**

¼ teaspoon **salt**

Freshly **ground pepper**, to taste

1 small head **romaine lettuce**, shredded (about 8 cups)

Smoked Turkey with Creamy Carrot and Raisin Salad

PREP	20 MINUTES
COOK	NONE
SERVES	4

1 Combine the sour cream, lemon zest, lemon juice, sugar, and salt in a large bowl. Add the carrots, turkey, and raisins; mix well.

2 Divide the greens evenly among 4 plates. Spoon the carrot-turkey mixture on top, then sprinkle with the pecans. Serve at once.

PER SERVING (scant 2 cups greens, 1 cup carrot-turkey mixture, and 1 tablespoon pecans): 199 Cal, 9 g Fat, 2 g Sat Fat, 0 g Trans Fat, 28 mg Chol, 696 mg Sod, 22 g Carb, 4 g Fib, 10 g Prot, 75 mg Calc. *POINTS* value: *4.*

EXPRESS LANE It takes 3 or 4 minutes to shred the carrots here with a box grater, but if time is of the essence, you could use 2 (6-ounce) bags of shredded carrots (from the produce section of the supermarket) instead. However, shredding your own carrots gives a finer texture and a juicier finish to the salad.

⅓ cup **light sour cream**

1 teaspoon grated **lemon zest**

1 tablespoon fresh **lemon juice**

¾ teaspoon **sugar**

¼ teaspoon **salt**

5–6 **carrots**, shredded (about 3 cups)

1 (6-ounce) piece **fully cooked smoked turkey breast**, cut into ½-inch chunks

⅓ cup **raisins**

1 (5-ounce) bag **mixed baby salad greens**

4 tablespoons coarsely chopped **pecans**

Fruited Couscous and Ham Salad

PREP	10 MINUTES PLUS 5 MINUTES STANDING TIME
COOK	ABOUT 5 MINUTES
SERVES	4

1 Bring the broth to a boil in a medium saucepan. Add the couscous, cover, and remove from the heat. Let stand 5 minutes then fluff with a fork.

2 Whisk the orange juice, vinegar, mustard, and honey in a medium bowl; add the apple and shallot; toss to coat. Add the couscous and ham; mix well.

3 Divide the spinach evenly among 4 plates. Spoon the couscous mixture on top and serve at once.

PER SERVING (2 cups spinach and 1¼ cups couscous mixture): 283 Cal, 4 g Fat, 1 g Sat Fat, 0 g Trans Fat, 20 mg Chol, 774 mg Sod, 47 g Carb, 4 g Fib, 16 g Prot, 71 mg Calc. **POINTS** value: **5.**

FOOD NOTE If you prefer to prepare the couscous mixture ahead of time, cover and refrigerate it for up to 24 hours, then let it sit at room temperature for 15 minutes before serving on the spinach.

- 1 cup **reduced-sodium chicken broth**
- 1 cup **couscous**
- ⅓ cup **orange juice**
- 3 tablespoons **cider vinegar**
- 1 tablespoon **Dijon mustard**
- 1 tablespoon **honey**
- 1 small **red apple**, diced
- 1 **shallot**, finely chopped
- 1 cup diced **cooked ham**
- 1 (6-ounce) bag **baby spinach leaves**

Warm Salmon Salad with Buttermilk-Scallion Dressing

PREP	20 MINUTES
COOK	ABOUT 20 MINUTES
SERVES	4

1 To make the Buttermilk-Scallion Dressing, combine the buttermilk, scallions, mustard, lemon zest, salt, and pepper in a small bowl.

2 To make the salad, combine the salmon, onion, parsley, and lemon juice in a large bowl.

3 Bring a medium saucepan two-thirds full of water to a boil. Add the potatoes and cook 6 minutes. Add the green beans and cook until the potatoes are just cooked through and the green beans are crisp-tender, about 6 minutes.

4 Drain the potatoes and beans in a colander; add to the salmon mixture. Add Buttermilk-Scallion Dressing; mix well.

5 Arrange the arugula on 4 salad plates, top each serving with one-quarter of the warm salmon mixture; arrange the tomatoes and olives on the side. Serve at once.

PER SERVING (2 cups): 246 Cal, 5 g Fat, 0 g Sat Fat, 0 g Trans Fat, 31 mg Chol, 552 mg Sod, 37 g Carb, 6 g Fib, 18 g Prot, 183 mg Calc.
POINTS value: **5.**

¾ cup **fat-free buttermilk**

3 **scallions**, finely chopped

2 teaspoons **whole-grain Dijon mustard**

1 teaspoon grated **lemon zest**

¼ teaspoon **salt**

¼ teaspoon freshly **ground pepper**

1 (7½-ounce) **can salmon**, drained and flaked

½ cup thinly sliced **red onion**

⅓ cup chopped fresh **flat-leaf parsley**

2 tablespoons fresh **lemon juice**

1 pound small **red potatoes**, scrubbed and chopped

½ pound fresh **green beans**, trimmed and cut into 2-inch lengths

2 large bunches **arugula**, tough stems discarded (about 8 cups)

3 large **plum tomatoes**, cut into wedges

8 **brine-cured black olives**

Chicory and Lentil Salad with Slow-Roasted Salmon

PREP	15 MINUTES
COOK	ABOUT 30 MINUTES
SERVES	4

1 Preheat the oven to 300°F. Line a baking sheet with foil.

2 Bring the water to a boil in a medium saucepan. Add the lentils and cook until just tender but still hold their shape, about 15 minutes. Drain and keep warm.

3 Put the salmon on the baking sheet skin-side down; sprinkle with ½ teaspoon of the salt and the ground pepper. Bake until just opaque in the center, 15–20 minutes.

4 Meanwhile, puree the bell pepper, broth, vinegar, and the remaining ½ teaspoon salt in a blender until smooth. With the motor running, add the oil through the feed tube and pulse until creamy. Transfer to a large bowl. Stir in the lentils, chicory, tomatoes, and shallot.

5 Lift the salmon away from its skin, divide into 4 equal portions, and transfer to a platter or serving plates. Serve the salmon hot with the warm chicory-lentil salad.

PER SERVING (3 ounces salmon with 1¼ cups salad): 380 Cal, 12 g Fat, 3 g Sat Fat, 0 Trans Fat, 74 mg Chol, 690 mg Sod, 32 g Carb, 12 g Fib, 37 g Prot, 56 mg Calc. **POINTS** value: **8.**

GOOD IDEA You can also serve this salad cold; prepare as the recipe directs, but cool the lentils under cold running water in a colander before adding to the remaining ingredients and let the salmon chill in the refrigerator for 2 to 3 hours.

4 cups **water**

1 cup **lentils**, picked over, rinsed, and drained

1 pound center-cut **salmon fillet**

1 teaspoon **salt**

¼ teaspoon freshly **ground pepper**

½ **yellow bell pepper**, seeded and cut into chunks

¼ cup **reduced-sodium chicken broth**

1¼ teaspoons **white-wine vinegar**

4 teaspoons **extra-virgin olive oil**

2 cups chopped **chicory**

1 cup diced **plum tomatoes**

2 tablespoons minced **shallot**

Chicory and Lentil Salad
with Slow-Roasted Salmon

Shrimp-Basil Tabbouleh Salad

Shrimp-Basil Tabbouleh Salad

PREP	20 MINUTES PLUS 25-30 MINUTES STANDING TIME
COOK	ABOUT 10 MINUTES
SERVES	4

1 Bring the water to a boil in a large saucepan. Stir in the bulgur; remove the pan from the heat. Cover and let stand until the water is absorbed, 25-30 minutes.

2 Meanwhile, fill a large bowl halfway with ice water. Put the shrimp in a steamer basket; set in a saucepan over 1 inch of boiling water. Cover tightly and steam until the shrimp are just opaque in the center, about 5 minutes. Plunge the shrimp into the ice water to stop cooking, drain, and coarsely chop. Set aside.

3 Fluff the bulgur with a fork; let cool slightly. Stir in the shrimp, cucumber, tomatoes, onion, basil, and parsley until just combined.

4 Combine the lime juice, oil, mustard, salt, and pepper in a small bowl until blended. Pour the dressing over the bulgur mixture; toss to coat. Serve at once.

PER SERVING (1½ cups): 232 Cal, 6 g Fat, 1 g Sat Fat, 0 g Trans Fat, 80 mg Chol, 433 mg Sod, 33 g Carb, 8 g Fib, 14 g Prot, 59 mg Calc.
POINTS value: **4.**

☑

1¼ cups **water**

1 cup **bulgur**

¾ pound medium **shrimp**, peeled and deveined

1 **cucumber**, peeled, seeded, and chopped

12 **cherry tomatoes**, quartered

1 small **red onion**, finely chopped

¼ cup chopped **fresh basil**

¼ cup chopped **fresh parsley**

3 tablespoons fresh **lime juice**

4 teaspoons **extra-virgin olive oil**

2 teaspoons **Dijon mustard**

½ teaspoon **salt**

½ teaspoon freshly **ground pepper**

Chopped Salad with Tuna and Bell Peppers

PREP	20 MINUTES
COOK	NONE
SERVES	4

Combine the broth, shallots, parsley, oil, vinegar, mustard, salt, and ground pepper in a large bowl. Add the lettuce, arugula, bell peppers, tuna, tomatoes, beans, and onion; mix well.

PER SERVING (2 cups): 214 Cal, 6 g Fat, 1 g Sat Fat, 0 g Trans Fat, 30 mg Chol, 678 mg Sod, 21 g Carb, 6 g Fib, 23 g Prot, 100 mg Calc.
POINTS value: ***4.***

FOOD NOTE Flaxseed oil—available in natural-foods stores and, increasingly, in supermarkets—is the best available plant source of Omega-3 fatty acids, and according to the USDA, contains anticancer agents. Flaxseed oil must be kept in your refrigerator; if not it quickly becomes rancid. It is best not to cook with it, but to add it to raw or already cooked food.

½ cup **reduced-sodium chicken broth**

2 **shallots**, finely chopped

3 tablespoons finely chopped **fresh flat-leaf parsley**

1 tablespoon **flaxseed oil**

2 teaspoons **balsamic vinegar**

1 teaspoon **Dijon mustard**

¼ teaspoon **salt**

¼ teaspoon freshly **ground pepper**

3 cups finely shredded **romaine lettuce**

3 cups finely shredded **arugula leaves**

1 **yellow bell pepper**, seeded and finely chopped

1 **green bell pepper**, seeded and finely chopped

2 (6-ounce) cans water-packed **solid white tuna**, drained

3 **plum tomatoes**, seeded and finely chopped

1 cup canned **small white beans**, rinsed and drained

1 small **red onion**, finely chopped

Tuna, Tomato, and Bean Salad

PREP	20 MINUTES
COOK	NONE
SERVES	4

1 Whisk the vinegar, oil, sage, pepper, and salt in a large bowl. Add the tomatoes and onion; toss to coat.

2 Break the tuna into large chunks and stir into the tomato mixture. Gently stir in the beans.

3 Place a lettuce leaf on each of 4 plates. Spoon about 1 cup of the salad on each plate.

PER SERVING (1 salad): 330 Cal, 7 g Fat, 1 g Sat Fat, 0 g Trans Fat, 26 mg Chol, 867 mg Sod, 36 g Carb, 9 g Fib, 32 g Prot, 106 mg Calc.
POINTS value: **6.**

FOOD NOTE Malt vinegar is a mild vinegar made from malted barley and popular in England, sprinkled on fish and chips. Cider vinegar makes a suitable substitute.

2 tablespoons **malt vinegar**

1½ tablespoons **extra-virgin olive oil**

1 teaspoon **dried sage** or **oregano**

½ teaspoon coarsely **ground pepper**

¼ teaspoon **salt**

2 cups **grape** or **cherry tomatoes,** halved

1 small **red onion,** finely chopped (about ½ cup)

2 (6-ounce) cans **solid white tuna** in water, drained

1 (15½-ounce) can small **white** or **navy beans,** rinsed and drained

4 large **Boston lettuce** leaves

Dilled Beet and White Bean Salad

PREP	15 MINUTES
COOK	NONE
SERVES	4

1 Whisk together the vinegar, mustard, oil, and salt in a large bowl until blended. Add the beans, bell pepper, onion, and dill; mix well.

2 Divide the greens evenly among 4 plates. Spoon the bean mixture on top. Surround the bean mixture with the beets.

PER SERVING (2½ cups greens, 1 cup bean mixture, and ¼ cup beets): 283 Cal, 4 g Fat, 0 g Sat Fat, 0 g Trans Fat, 0 mg Chol, 1107 mg Sod, 50 g Carb, 13 g Fib, 15 g Prot, 153 mg Calc. **POINTS** value: **5.**

3 tablespoons white-balsamic vinegar

2 teaspoons Dijon mustard

2 teaspoons flaxseed oil

½ teaspoon salt

2 (15½-ounce) cans white navy beans, rinsed and drained

1 orange bell pepper, seeded and chopped

¼ cup finely chopped red onion

¼ cup chopped fresh dill

1 (8-ounce) bag Mediterranean-blend salad greens (romaine, chicory, and radicchio)

1 (14½-ounce) can sliced beets, drained

Meatless Chef's Salad

PREP	20 MINUTES PLUS 15 MINUTES STANDING TIME
COOK	NONE
SERVES	4

1 Combine the vinegar, oil, garlic, and Italian seasoning in a small bowl. Add the sun-dried tomatoes and toss to coat. Marinate at least 15 minutes, tossing occasionally. (This step can be done up to 2 days ahead; just cover and refrigerate.)

2 To assemble the salad, toss the lettuce with the dressing in a large bowl. Arrange the following ingredients on top, each in its own section: cucumber slices, marinated sun-dried tomatoes, eggs, tomato wedges, and cheese. Sprinkle with pepper and serve at once.

PER SERVING (3½ cups): 176 Cal, 8 g Fat, 2 g Sat Fat, 0 g Trans Fat, 112 mg Chol, 539 mg Sod, 16 g Carb, 4 g Fib, 13 g Prot, 222 mg Calc. **POINTS** value: **3.**

GOOD IDEA If your sun-dried tomatoes aren't soft enough to chew easily, place in a heatproof bowl and pour in enough hot water to cover. Let stand until softened, about 10 minutes. Drain well, pressing out the water and patting the tomatoes dry with paper towels. Then proceed with the recipe at Step 1.

2 tablespoons **balsamic vinegar**

1 tablespoon **extra-virgin olive oil**

1 small **garlic clove**, minced

¼ teaspoon **Italian seasoning**

½ cup (about 20) **sun-dried tomato halves** (not oil-packed), sliced into thin strips

2 small heads **romaine, iceberg,** or other **lettuce,** cleaned and chopped into bite-size pieces (about 8 cups)

⅓ cup **fat-free Italian, Ranch,** or **Thousand Island dressing**

1 small **cucumber,** thinly sliced

4 large **hard-cooked eggs** (2 yolks removed for another use), finely chopped

2 ripe **tomatoes,** sliced into wedges

2 ounces **fat-free Swiss cheese,** cut into thin strips

Freshly **ground pepper,** to taste

Belgian Endive and Pear Salad

PREP	20 MINUTES
COOK	NONE
SERVES	4

1 Combine the vinegar, cilantro, oil, shallot, mustard, salt, and pepper in a medium bowl. Add the pear and toss gently to coat.

2 Separate 12 outer leaves from the heads of endive. Chop the remaining endive and mix with the pear and dressing. Arrange the endive leaves on 4 plates. Spoon the pear mixture over the endive leaves and serve at once.

PER SERVING (3 endive leaves with ½ cup pear mixture): 49 Cal, 4 g Fat, 1 g Sat Fat, 0 g Trans Fat, 0 mg Chol, 164 mg Sod, 5 g Carb, 2 g Fib, 0 g Prot, 10 mg Calc. **POINTS** value: *1.*

HOW WE DID IT To prevent the pear from turning brown from exposure to the air, make the dressing before you core and slice the pear and add the pear to the dressing right away.

2 tablespoons **red-wine vinegar**

2 tablespoons chopped **fresh cilantro**

1 tablespoon **olive oil**

1 tablespoon minced **shallot**

½ teaspoon **Dijon mustard**

¼ teaspoon **salt**

⅛ teaspoon freshly **ground pepper**

1 ripe **pear**, cored and sliced

2 large heads **Belgian endive**

Belgian Endive and Pear Salad

New Potato, Beet, and Apple Salad

PREP	20 MINUTES PLUS 1 HOUR CHILLING TIME
COOK	ABOUT 25 MINUTES
SERVES	6

1 Combine the beets, potatoes, apples, pickles, and onion in a serving bowl (or arrange in sections on a serving platter).

2 Combine the vinegar, oil, ½ teaspoon of the salt, and the black pepper in a small bowl or measuring cup; drizzle over the salad. Scatter the parsley around the edges of the salad; cover and refrigerate until chilled, at least 1 hour.

3 Just before serving, make the dressing: Combine the sour cream, lemon juice, the reserved beet juice, the white pepper, and the remaining ¼ teaspoon salt. Serve with the salad, on the side.

PER SERVING (1 cup salad with 1 generous tablespoon dressing): 123 Cal, 3 g Fat, 0 g Sat Fat, 0 g Trans Fat, 3 mg Chol, 582 mg Sod, 23 g Carb, 3 g Fib, 3 g Prot, 63 mg Calc. **POINTS** value: **2.**

GOOD IDEA Crunchy breadsticks go well with this salad. Just remember to deduct them from your weekly **POINTS** Allowance, 4 (5-inch) bread sticks for each serving will increase the **POINTS** value by 2).

3 cups finely diced cooked or canned **beets** (reserve 1 tablespoon cooking liquid or can liquid, for the dressing)

8 ounces cooked **red potatoes** (scant 2 cups), peeled, if desired, and diced

2 small **tart apples** (such as Granny Smith), peeled and diced

⅓ cup finely chopped **unsweetened pickles**

⅓ medium **sweet onion**, finely chopped

3 tablespoons **white vinegar**

1 tablespoon **canola oil**

¾ teaspoon **salt**

½ teaspoon freshly **ground pepper**

3 tablespoons chopped **fresh parsley** or **dill**

½ cup **fat-free sour cream**

2 teaspoons fresh **lemon juice**

¼ teaspoon ground **white pepper**

Sugar Snap Pea Salad

PREP	15 MINUTES
COOK	COOK TIME: ABOUT 5 MINUTES
SERVES	4

1 Put the sugar snap peas in a steamer basket; set in a saucepan over 1 inch of boiling water. Cover tightly and steam the sugar snap peas just until bright green, about 2 minutes. Rinse under cold running water; drain well and transfer to a serving bowl.

2 Meanwhile, to make the dressing, slice the tomato in half and grate each half over a 1-cup glass measure, using the coarse side of a box grater (you'll get about ¼ cup of thick juice). Whisk in the oil, vinegar, and garlic with a fork.

3 Pour the dressing over the cooled peas and sprinkle with the dill; toss well. Serve at once.

PER SERVING (1 cup): 86 Cal, 3 g Fat, 0 g Sat Fat, 0 g Trans Fat, 0 mg Chol, 9 mg Sod, 12 g Carb, 4 g Fib, 5 g Prot, 62 mg Calc. *POINTS* value: *1.*

GOOD IDEA Dress the salad just before serving; the acid in the vinaigrette will turn the peas a drab olive color if the salad is allowed to stand longer than 30 minutes.

4 cups fresh **sugar snap peas**, trimmed

1 ripe **tomato**

2 teaspoons **olive** or **canola oil**

1 teaspoon **red-wine vinegar**

1 small **garlic clove**, minced

1 tablespoon chopped **fresh dill**

**Green Bean and Corn Salad with
Tomato-Tarragon Vinaigrette**

Green Bean and Corn Salad with Tomato-Tarragon Vinaigrette

PREP	15 MINUTES PLUS 30 MINUTES STANDING TIME
COOK	ABOUT 15 MINUTES
SERVES	6

1 Bring a large pot of water to a boil. Add the green beans and return to a boil. Cook 2 minutes. Add the corn and cook until the green beans and corn are crisp-tender, about 1 minute. Rinse the vegetables under cold running water; drain well.

2 Combine the vinegar, oil, mayonnaise, water, pepper, and salt in a large bowl. Stir in the tomato, shallot, tarragon, and chives. Add the green beans and corn; mix well. Let stand at room temperature about 30 minutes before serving to blend the flavors.

PER SERVING (1 cup): 81 Cal, 2 g Fat, 0 g Sat Fat, 0 g Trans Fat, 0 mg Chol, 121 mg Sod, 15 g Carb, 4 g Fib, 3 g Prot, 45 mg Calc. **POINTS** value: *1.*

GOOD IDEA If you make this salad when corn and beefsteak tomatoes are not in season, use 3 plum tomatoes and 1 cup frozen corn kernels, thawed (and skip cooking the corn in Step 1).

1 pound fresh **green beans**, trimmed and cut in half

1 cup fresh **corn kernels**

2 tablespoons **white-wine vinegar**

2 teaspoons **olive oil**

2 teaspoons **fat-free mayonnaise**

2 teaspoons **water**

½ teaspoon freshly **ground pepper**

¼ teaspoon **salt**

1 beefsteak **tomato**, diced

1 large **shallot**, minced

3 tablespoons chopped **fresh tarragon**

3 tablespoons chopped fresh **chives**

Warm Cabbage Salad

PREP	10 MINUTES
COOK	ABOUT 10 MINUTES
SERVES	4

Spray a large deep nonstick skillet with nonstick spray and set over medium heat. Add the ginger and garlic; cook, stirring constantly, until softened and fragrant, about 2 minutes. Add the cabbage, carrots, salt, and cayenne; cook, stirring occasionally, until the cabbage is softened, about 6 minutes. Stir in the scallions and vinegar; cook, stirring frequently, until the cabbage is tender, about 3 minutes.

PER SERVING (1 cup): 51 Cal, 0 g Fat, 0 g Sat Fat, 0 g Trans Fat, 0 mg Chol, 179 mg Sod, 9 g Carb, 4 g Fib, 3 g Prot, 104 mg Calc. **POINTS** value: **0.**

FOOD NOTE Napa cabbage, also called Chinese cabbage, is a mild-tasting variety of cabbage with crisp, crinkly, thin leaves. It's nutritious too, as a good source of vitamin A, folic acid, and potassium.

1 tablespoon very thin 1-inch strips peeled **fresh ginger**

1–2 **garlic cloves**, thinly sliced

8 cups shredded **napa cabbage**

1 cup matchstick-size **carrots**

¼ teaspoon **salt**

⅛ teaspoon **cayenne**

6 **scallions**, finely chopped

2 teaspoons **rice vinegar**

Hot Apple Slaw

PREP	10 MINUTES
COOK	ABOUT 18 MINUTES
SERVES	4

4 teaspoons **canola oil**

1 **onion**, very thinly sliced

1 small head **red cabbage**, very thinly sliced (about 5 cups)

½ teaspoon **salt**

2 medium **tart apples**, sliced into wedges

1 tablespoon slivered **fresh sage**, or 1 teaspoon crumbled dried

1 tablespoon **cider vinegar**

1 tablespoon **Dijon mustard**

1 Heat the oil a large nonstick skillet over medium-high heat. Add the onion and cook, stirring occasionally, until softened, about 5 minutes.

2 Add the cabbage and salt; cook, stirring occasionally, until the cabbage is tender, 6–8 minutes. Stir in the apples, sage, vinegar, and mustard; cook, stirring gently, until the apples are just tender (they'll be slightly pink), about 5 minutes.

PER SERVING (1 cup): 122 Cal, 6 g Fat, 0 g Sat Fat, 0 g Trans Fat, 0 mg Chol, 396 mg Sod, 19 g Carb, 4 g Fib, 2 g Prot, 64 mg Calc. ***POINTS** value: **2.***

GOOD IDEA We suggest Granny Smith apples in this recipe for their bright green skin and tart flavor, but golden-fleshed Jonathans or Baldwins work well, too. Although the slaw is best hot out of the skillet, it's also great at room temperature or slightly chilled.

Scandinavian Slaw

PREP	20 MINUTES
COOK	NONE
SERVES	6

Combine the buttermilk, mayonnaise, dill, horseradish, pepper, salt, and caraway seeds in a large bowl. Add the green and red cabbages, cucumber, carrots, scallions, and radishes; mix well.

PER SERVING (1 cup): 43 Cal, 1 g Fat, 0 g Sat Fat, 0 g Trans Fat, 2 mg Chol, 199 mg Sod, 8 g Carb, 2 g Fib, 3 g Prot, 85 mg Calc.
POINTS value: *1.*

EXPRESS LANE If you want to save time, use prepared coleslaw mix in place of the shredded cabbage and carrots.

1 cup **fat-free buttermilk**

3 tablespoons **fat-free mayonnaise**

3 tablespoons chopped **fresh dill**

1 tablespoon prepared **horseradish**

½ teaspoon freshly **ground pepper**

¼ teaspoon **salt**

¼ teaspoon **caraway seeds**

2 cups shredded **green cabbage**

2 cups shredded **red cabbage**

½ seedless **cucumber**, quartered lengthwise and thinly sliced

½ cup shredded **carrots**

3 **scallions**, sliced

3 **radishes**, cut in half and sliced

Scandinavian Slaw

CHAPTER 4

Succulent Steaks, Chops, and More

Steak and Potatoes

PREP	10 MINUTES
COOK	ABOUT 40 MINUTES
SERVES	4

1 Preheat the oven to 425°F. Spray a baking sheet with olive oil nonstick spray.

2 Arrange the potatoes about 2 inches apart on the sheet in a single layer. Generously spray with olive oil nonstick spray. Roast until browned and crisp, about 20 minutes on each side. Transfer to a bowl. Add the parsley, cumin, ¼ teaspoon of the salt, and ⅛ teaspoon of the pepper; toss well.

3 Meanwhile, sprinkle the steaks with the remaining ½ teaspoon salt and ⅛ teaspoon pepper. Spray a ridged grill pan with olive oil nonstick spray and set over medium-high heat. Add the steaks and cook until an instant-read thermometer inserted in the center of each steak registers 145°F for medium-rare, about 4 minutes on each side, or 160°F for medium, about 6 minutes on each side. Serve with the potatoes.

PER SERVING (½ steak with 2 potato wedges): 254 Cal, 9 g Fat, 3 g Sat Fat, 1 g Trans Fat, 50 mg Chol, 500 mg Sod, 20 g Carb, 2 g Fib, 23 g Prot, 23 mg Calc. **POINTS** value: **5.**

- 2 (8-ounce) **baking potatoes**, scrubbed and quartered lengthwise
- 1 tablespoon chopped **fresh parsley**
- ½ teaspoon ground **cumin**
- ¾ teaspoon **salt**
- ¼ teaspoon freshly **ground pepper**
- 2 (¾-pound) **T-bone steaks**, ¾ inch thick, trimmed of visible fat

Prime Rib with Mushroom Sauce

PREP	10 MINUTES
COOK	ABOUT 20 MINUTES
SERVES	4

1 Preheat the oven to 550°F. Spray a large cast-iron skillet with nonstick spray and set over high heat.

2 Meanwhile, sprinkle the steak with the salt and pepper. Add the steak to the skillet and cook, shaking the pan once or twice to prevent sticking, about 5 minutes. Turn the steak over, then place the skillet in the oven. Roast until an instant-read thermometer inserted in the center of the steak registers 145°F for medium-rare, about 7 minutes. Transfer the steak to a plate and cover lightly with foil.

3 Return the skillet to medium-high heat. Add the onion and cook, stirring, until translucent, about 1 minute. Add the mushrooms and garlic; cook, stirring, until fragrant, about 1 minute. Add the broth and sherry; cook, scraping up any browned bits from the bottom of the skillet, about 1 minute. Cut the meat off the bone, then carve into ½-inch-thick slices against the grain and serve with the sauce.

PER SERVING (4 slices steak and ¼ cup sauce): 203 Cal, 8 g Fat, 3 g Sat Fat, 0 g Trans Fat, 66 mg Chol, 686 mg Sod, 4 g Carb, 1 g Fib, 26 g Prot, 18 mg Calc. *POINTS* value: *5.*

GOOD IDEA Do not use a nonstick skillet for this recipe. Most nonstick coatings are not made for high temperatures. A cast-iron skillet works best, although a stainless steel skillet will do the trick as well. And watch the handle—if yours is made of wood or rubber, wrap it well in foil before placing the skillet in the oven.

1 (1¾-pound) **bone-in rib steak**, about 2 inches thick, trimmed of visible fat

1 teaspoon **salt**

Freshly **ground pepper**

1 small **onion**, chopped

2 cups thinly sliced **fresh white** or **cremini mushrooms**

2 **garlic cloves**, minced

¼ cup **reduced-sodium chicken broth**

2 tablespoons **sherry** or **dry vermouth**

Fennel-and-Onion
Smothered Steak

Fennel-and-Onion Smothered Steak

PREP	**15 MINUTES**
COOK	**ABOUT 20 MINUTES**
SERVES	**4**

1 Heat 2 teaspoons of the oil in a large nonstick skillet over medium-high heat. Add the fennel, onion, garlic, tarragon, ¼ teaspoon of the salt, and ⅛ teaspoon of the pepper; cook, stirring occasionally, until fennel and onion are very soft and golden, about 11 minutes. Add the broth and cook until almost evaporated, about 5 minutes. Transfer to a bowl.

2 Sprinkle the steaks with the remaining ½ teaspoon salt and ⅛ teaspoon pepper. Heat the remaining 1 teaspoon oil in the same skillet over medium-high heat. Add the steaks and cook until browned, about 2 minutes on each side. Add the fennel mixture and cook, stirring constantly to scrape the browned bits from the bottom of the skillet, until the steaks are done to taste and the liquid thickens, about 1 minute for medium-rare or about 3 minutes for well done. Serve at once.

PER SERVING (½ steak with about ¼ cup fennel mixture): 206 Cal, 10 g Fat, 3 g Sat Fat, 1 g Trans Fat, 49 mg Chol, 624 mg Sod, 8 g Carb, 2 g Fib, 21 g Prot, 47 mg Calc. **POINTS** value: **5.**

GOOD IDEA Lean sirloin benefits from a shorter cooking time to stay tender. So if you prefer your steak well done, cut the sirloin into very thin slices or substitute beef tenderloin in the recipe.

3 teaspoons olive oil

1 large fennel bulb, thinly sliced

1 large onion, thinly sliced

4 garlic cloves, sliced

¼ teaspoon dried tarragon

¾ teaspoon salt

¼ teaspoon freshly ground pepper

1 cup reduced-sodium beef broth

2 (½-pound) boneless sirloin steaks, trimmed of visible fat and each cut crosswise in half

Herb-Marinated Steak

PREP	10 MINUTES PLUS 2 HOURS CHILLING AND 5 MINUTES STANDING TIME
COOK	ABOUT 15 MINUTES
SERVES	6

1 To make the marinade, combine the vinegar, soy sauce, lemon juice, oil, garlic, oregano, basil, and thyme in a zip-close plastic bag; add the steak. Squeeze out the air and seal the bag; turn to coat the steak. Refrigerate, turning the bag occasionally, at least 2 hours or up to 8 hours.

2 Spray the grill rack with nonstick spray; prepare the grill. Remove the steak from the marinade; discard any remaining marinade. Place the steak on the grill rack. Sprinkle with the salt and pepper. Grill the steak until an instant-read thermometer inserted in the center of the steak registers 145°F for medium-rare, about 6 minutes on each side. Transfer the steak to a cutting board and let stand about 5 minutes. Cut the steak on an angle against the grain into 18 thin slices.

PER SERVING (3 slices): 126 Cal, 4 g Fat, 1 g Sat Fat, 1 g Trans Fat, 54 mg Chol, 478 mg Sod, 1 g Carb, 0 g Fib, 21 g Prot, 8 mg Calc.
POINTS value: *3.*

3 tablespoons **red-wine vinegar**

2 tablespoons **reduced-sodium soy sauce**

2 tablespoons fresh **lemon juice**

4 teaspoons **extra-virgin olive oil**

2 **garlic cloves**, minced

1 teaspoon **dried oregano**

1 teaspoon **dried basil**

¼ teaspoon **dried thyme**

1 (1¼-pound) **top round steak** or **London broil**, trimmed of visible fat

1 teaspoon **salt**

¼ teaspoon freshly **ground pepper**

Grilled Flank Steak with Chimichurri

☑

PREP	10 MINUTES PLUS 5 MINUTES STANDING TIME
COOK	ABOUT 10 MINUTES
SERVES	6

1 Spray the grill rack with nonstick spray; prepare the grill.

2 Meanwhile, to make the chimichurri, combine the lime juice, cilantro, parsley, garlic, oil, lime zest, and ½ teaspoon of the salt in a small bowl; set aside.

3 Combine the Mexican seasoning, chili powder, and the remaining ½ teaspoon salt in another small bowl. Rub the seasoning mixture over both sides of the steak.

4 Place the steak on the grill rack and close the grill. Grill the steak until an instant-read thermometer inserted in the center of the steak registers 145°F for medium-rare, about 5 minutes on each side. Transfer the steak to a cutting board and let stand about 5 minutes. Slice thinly on an angle against the grain into 18 slices. Serve with the chimichurri.

PER SERVING (3 slices steak with 4 teaspoons chimichurri): 169 Cal, 9 g Fat, 3 g Sat Fat, 1 g Trans Fat, 45 mg Chol, 541 mg Sod, 2 g Carb, 0 g Fib, 19 g Prot, 11 mg Calc. **POINTS** value: **4.**

EXPRESS LANE To get a head start on dinner prep, make the chimichurri sauce and refrigerate in an airtight container one day ahead.

¼ cup fresh **lime juice**

3 tablespoons chopped **fresh cilantro**

3 tablespoons chopped **fresh parsley**

1 **garlic clove**, minced

1 tablespoon **extra-virgin olive oil**

1 teaspoon grated **lime zest**

1 teaspoon **salt**

1 tablespoon **Mexican seasoning**

½ teaspoon **chipotle chili powder**

1 (1¼-pound) **flank steak**, trimmed of visible fat

Steak au Poivre

PREP	5 MINUTES
COOK	10 MINUTES
SERVES	4

1 Sprinkle the steaks with the salt. Press the pepper onto both sides of each steak. Heat 2 teaspoons of the oil in a large nonstick skillet over medium-high heat. Add the steaks and cook until an instant-read thermometer inserted in the center of the steak registers 145°F for medium-rare, about 3 minutes on each side. Transfer the steaks to a plate.

2 Heat the remaining 1 teaspoon oil in the same skillet over medium-high heat. Add the onion, garlic, and thyme; cook, stirring frequently, until slightly softened, about 2 minutes. Add broth and bring to a boil; cook until mixture reduces by about one-third, about 3 minutes. Stir in the mustard.

3 Add the steaks with any accumulated juices to the skillet. Cook until heated through, about 30 seconds on each side.

PER SERVING (1 steak with 3 tablespoons sauce): 163 Cal, 9 g Fat, 2 g Sat Fat, 1 g Trans Fat, 43 mg Chol, 500 mg Sod, 5 g Carb, 1 g Fib, 16 g Prot, 20 mg Calc. **POINTS** value: **4.**

GOOD IDEA If you prefer your steaks a little less spicy, reduce the pepper to a scant ½ teaspoon. You'll still get a great robust-tasting sauce.

4 (3-ounce) beef tenderloin steaks, ¾-inch thick, trimmed of visible fat

½ teaspoon salt

¾ teaspoon coarsely ground black pepper

3 teaspoons extra-virgin olive oil

1 onion, chopped

2 garlic cloves, minced

1½ teaspoons minced fresh thyme or ½ teaspoon dried

1 cup reduced-sodium beef broth

2 teaspoons Dijon mustard

Thai Beef Sauté

PREP	10 MINUTES
COOK	ABOUT 10 MINUTES
SERVES	4

1 **pound beef tenderloin**, trimmed of visible fat and cut into 2 x ¼-inch strips

2 tablespoons shredded **unsweetened coconut**, ground in a spice grinder or mini food processor

1 teaspoon **cinnamon**

¼ teaspoon **ground star anise** or **five-spice powder**

6 large **radishes**, thinly sliced

¼ cup **reduced-sodium chicken** or **beef broth**

2 tablespoons **Asian fish sauce** (nam pla)

1½ tablespoons bottled **Asian red chile sauce**

1 Toss the beef, coconut, cinnamon, and star anise in a medium bowl until the beef is coated.

2 Spray a large nonstick skillet with nonstick spray and set over medium-high heat. Add the beef and cook, stirring occasionally, until browned, about 4 minutes. Transfer the beef to a plate.

3 Add the radishes to the skillet and cook, stirring, until softened, about 2 minutes. Add the broth, fish sauce, and chile sauce; bring to a simmer, stirring to scrape up any browned bits from the bottom of the skillet.

4 Return the beef and any accumulated juices to the skillet. Reduce the heat to low and simmer until slightly thickened, about 2 minutes.

PER SERVING (1 cup): 208 Cal, 10 g Fat, 4 g Sat Fat, 0 g Trans Fat, 65 mg Chol, 877 mg Sod, 3 g Carb, 1 g Fib, 25 g Prot, 25 mg Calc. **POINTS** value: **5.**

FOOD NOTE Bottled chile sauce is a fiery combination of peppers and aromatic spices, usually bound with vinegar and sometimes sweetened with cane juice or sugar. It is sold under names like "sambal oelek" (a Chinese variety) or "sriracha chili sauce" (a Thai product). Add less if you're unsure of the heat—you can always add more later. Once opened, the bottled should be stored in the refrigerator, where it will keep for up to 1 year.

Sukiyaki Salad

PREP	10 MINUTES PLUS 3 MINUTES STANDING TIME
COOK	ABOUT 10 MINUTES
SERVES	4

1 Mix the powdered green tea, wasabi powder, and sugar on a plate. Press the steaks into the mixture to coat all sides.

2 Spray a large nonstick skillet with nonstick spray and set over medium-high heat. Add the steaks and cook, turning occasionally, until an instant-read thermometer inserted in the center of each steak registers 145°F for medium-rare, about 8 minutes, or 160°F for medium, about 10 minutes.

3 Meanwhile, place the slaw mix and mushrooms in a large bowl. Add the soy sauce, vinegar, olive oil, and sesame oil; toss to coat. Transfer the steaks to a cutting board and let stand about 3 minutes.

4 Slice the steaks into thin strips. Divide the salad among 4 plates, then top with steak slices.

PER SERVING (1½ cups salad and 1 sliced steak): 208 Cal, 10 g Fat, 3 g Sat Fat, 0 g Trans Fat, 48 mg Chol, 197 mg Sod, 10 g Carb, 3 g Fib, 21 g Prot, 65 mg Calc. *POINTS* value: *4.*

FOOD NOTE Powdered green tea is available in most natural-foods stores and many gourmet markets. You can also make your own by placing 4 teaspoons packed green tea leaves in a mini food processor or a spice grinder and pulsing until finely powdered. Wasabi powder is made from the pulverized root of horseradish and is available in gourmet markets, from Asian online retailers, and in the Asian aisle of many supermarkets.

1 tablespoon **powdered green tea**

2 teaspoons **wasabi powder**

1 teaspoon **sugar**

4 (3-ounce) **filet mignon** steaks or ¾ pound beef tenderloin, trimmed of visible fat and cut into 4 pieces

6 cups bagged **slaw mix**

1 (3½-ounce) package **fresh enoki mushrooms**, or ¼ pound sliced **white mushrooms**

1 tablespoon **reduced-sodium soy sauce**

1 tablespoon **white rice vinegar**

2 teaspoons **extra-virgin olive oil**

1 teaspoon **Asian** (dark) **sesame oil**

Sukiyaki Salad

Beef Bourguignon in a Flash

PREP	10 MINUTES
COOK	ABOUT 10 MINUTES
SERVES	4

1 Combine the beef and ground mushrooms in a medium bowl; toss to coat.

2 Spray a large nonstick saucepan with nonstick spray and set over medium-high heat. Add the beef and cook, turning occasionally, until browned, about 2 minutes. Add the mixed vegetables, thyme, and rosemary; cook, stirring frequently, about 1 minute.

3 Add the wine and bring to a boil, scraping up any browned bits from the bottom of the pan. Reduce the heat and simmer about 2 minutes.

4 Stir in the gravy, prunes, salt, and pepper; return to a boil. Reduce the heat to low and simmer until slightly thickened, about 5 minutes.

PER SERVING (1¼ cups): 288 Cal, 9 g Fat, 3 g Sat Fat, 0 g Trans Fat, 65 mg Chol, 718 mg Sod, 22 g Carb, 3 g Fib, 29 g Prot, 42 mg Calc. **POINTS** value: **6.**

FOOD NOTE Dried mushrooms are available in the produce section of most supermarkets. Look for light-colored stems and large pieces, not darkened mushrooms that have been crushed during improper storage. Porcinis work best here, although you could also use dried chanterelles or dried black trumpet mushrooms.

1 pound **beef tenderloin**, trimmed of visible fat and cut into 1-inch pieces

½ ounce **dried porcini mushrooms**, ground in a spice grinder or mini food processor

1 (12-ounce) package **frozen mixed vegetables**, preferably a mixture with pearl onions and carrots, thawed

1 teaspoon **dried thyme**

1 teaspoon **dried rosemary**, crumbled

⅔ cup **dry red wine**

1 cup **reduced-sodium fat-free canned beef gravy**

6 pitted **prunes**, halved

½ teaspoon **salt**

Freshly **ground pepper**, to taste

Dijon Beef Stroganoff

PREP	10 MINUTES
COOK	ABOUT 15 MINUTES
SERVES	4

1 Sprinkle the beef with ¼ teaspoon of the salt and ⅛ teaspoon of the pepper. Heat 2 teaspoons of the oil in a 12-inch nonstick skillet over medium-high heat. Add the beef and cook, stirring occasionally, until browned and cooked through, about 4 minutes. Transfer the beef to a plate.

2 Heat the remaining 1 teaspoon oil in the same skillet over medium-high heat. Add the mushrooms and the remaining ½ teaspoon salt and ⅛ teaspoon pepper; cook, stirring occasionally, until the mushrooms start to release their liquid, about 1 minute. Add the shallot and garlic; cook, stirring occasionally, until the shallot is softened and the mushrooms are browned, about 3 minutes. Stir in the broth and bring to a boil. Cook until the mixture is reduced by about one-half, about 6 minutes.

3 Stir in the beef and cook until heated through, about 1 minute. Remove the skillet from the heat; stir in the sour cream and mustard. Serve at once.

PER SERVING (about ⅔ cup): 188 Cal, 9 g Fat, 3 g Sat Fat, 1 g Trans Fat, 45 mg Chol, 750 mg Sod, 7 g Carb, 1 g Fib, 19 g Prot, 47 mg Calc. *POINTS* value: *4.*

GOOD IDEA To soak up all the delicious sauce, serve this dish over linguine (1 cup cooked whole-wheat pasta for each serving will increase the *POINTS* value by 3).

¾ pound **beef tenderloin**, trimmed of visible fat and cut into 1½-inch chunks

¾ teaspoon **salt**

¼ teaspoon freshly **ground pepper**

3 teaspoons **extra-virgin olive oil**

1 (8-ounce) package sliced **fresh mushrooms**

1 large **shallot**, minced

2 **garlic cloves**, minced

1½ cups **reduced-sodium beef broth**

⅓ cup **fat-free sour cream**

1 tablespoon **Dijon mustard**

Beef Yakitori Skewers

PREP	10 MINUTES PLUS 30 MINUTES STANDING TIME
COOK	ABOUT 10 MINUTES
SERVES	4

☑

¼ cup **reduced-sodium soy sauce**

1 tablespoon minced peeled **fresh ginger**

1 **garlic clove**, minced

¾ pound **beef tenderloin**, trimmed of visible fat and cut into 1-inch cubes

2 **scallions**, cut into 8 pieces each

1 Spray the grill rack with nonstick spray; prepare the grill. If using wooden skewers, soak them in water 30 minutes.

2 Combine the soy sauce, ginger, and garlic in a small bowl.

3 Alternately thread the beef and scallions onto 4 (10-inch) metal or wooden skewers. Place the skewers on the grill rack and close the grill. Grill about 3 minutes on each side. Brush both sides of the skewers with the soy sauce mixture. Grill until the beef is cooked as desired, about 30 seconds on each side for medium-rare, or about 1 minute on each side for well done.

PER SERVING (1 skewer): 132 Cal, 6 g Fat, 2 g Sat Fat, 1 g Trans Fat, 42 mg Chol, 638 mg Sod, 2 g Carb, 0 g Fib, 15 g Prot, 10 mg Calc. **POINTS** value: *3.*

GOOD IDEA Try this recipe with 4 (¼-pound) skinless boneless chicken thighs. Prepare as directed, except grill about 5 minutes on each side then brush with the soy sauce mixture and grill, turning once, until cooked through, about 2 minutes. (The **POINTS** value for each serving will be 4.)

Penne with Meat Sauce Arrabiata

PREP	10 MINUTES
COOK	ABOUT 25 MINUTES
SERVES	6

1 Spray a nonstick Dutch oven with olive oil nonstick spray and set over medium-high heat. Add the beef and cook, stirring frequently to break it up, until browned, about 5 minutes; transfer to a bowl.

2 Heat the oil in the same the Dutch oven over medium-high heat. Add the onion, bell pepper, garlic, basil, fennel, and crushed red pepper; cook, stirring occasionally, until slightly softened, about 3 minutes. Add the beef, tomatoes, tomato paste, and salt; bring to a boil. Reduce the heat and cook, stirring occasionally, until the sauce is slightly thickened, 15–18 minutes.

3 Meanwhile, cook the penne according to package directions; drain in a colander. Return the penne to the pot and stir in 1 cup of the sauce. Divide the pasta mixture among 6 plates and top each with the remaining sauce.

PER SERVING (about 1⅔ cups): 354 Cal, 6 g Fat, 2 g Sat Fat, 0 g Trans Fat, 32 mg Chol, 409 mg Sod, 58 g Carb, 9 g Fib, 23 g Prot, 86 mg Calc.
POINTS value: **7.**

GOOD IDEA If you like your pasta served with cheese, sprinkle 2 tablespoons freshly grated Parmesan cheese on each serving. Just remember to deduct it from your weekly **POINTS** Allowance (2 tablespoons will increase the **POINTS** value by 1).

¾ pound **ground lean beef** (5% or less fat)

2 teaspoons **extra-virgin olive oil**

1 **onion**, chopped

1 small **red bell pepper**, seeded and chopped

3 **garlic cloves**, minced

1 teaspoon **dried basil**

¼ teaspoon **ground fennel**

¼ teaspoon **crushed red pepper**

1 (28-ounce) **can crushed tomatoes**

¼ cup **tomato paste**

½ teaspoon **salt**

4 cups **whole-wheat penne** (about 12 ounces)

Fajitas

Fajitas

PREP	10 MINUTES
COOK	ABOUT 10 MINUTES
SERVES	4

1 Toss the beef strips with the chili powder, lime juice, garlic, salt, and ground pepper in a large bowl until well coated.

2 Spray a large nonstick skillet with nonstick spray and set over high heat. Add as many of the beef strips as will fit in one layer. Cook, turning once, about 2 minutes for rare, 3 minutes for medium-rare, or 4 minutes for medium. (Do not crowd the pan—if you do, the strips will steam and turn gray.) Transfer the beef strips to a plate and continue cooking the remaining beef strips.

3 Add the bell peppers and onion to the same skillet and cook, stirring, until slightly softened, about 2 minutes. Add the carrots and cook, stirring, 1 minute. Spoon 1 cup of the vegetables on top of a tortilla, top with the ½ cup beef strips, ½ cup lettuce, and 1 tablespoon sour cream. Repeat with the remaining tortillas, vegetables, beef, and toppings.

PER SERVING (1 fajita): 272 Cal, 4 g Fat, 1 g Sat Fat, 0 g Trans Fat, 61 mg Chol, 663 mg Sod, 31 g Carb, 7 g Fib, 28 g Prot, 99 mg Calc. **POINTS** value: **5.**

GOOD IDEA Serve with a fresh salsa of chopped tomatoes, red onion and cilantro, seasoned with a pinch of salt and cayenne.

1 pound **boneless sirloin steak**, trimmed of visible fat and cut into 2 x ¼-inch strips

1 tablespoon **chili powder**

1 tablespoon fresh **lime juice**

1 **garlic clove**, minced

½ teaspoon **salt**

Freshly **ground pepper**

2 **green bell peppers**, seeded and thinly sliced

1 **large red onion**, sliced into thin rings

2 large **carrots**, shredded

4 (6-inch) **fat-free whole-wheat flour tortillas**

2 cups purchased **salad mix** or shredded iceberg lettuce

¼ cup **fat-free sour cream**

Beef in Garlic Sauce

PREP	10 MINUTES
COOK	ABOUT 8 MINUTES
SERVES	4

1 Spray a large nonstick wok or high-sided skillet with nonstick spray and set over high heat until a drop of water sizzles. Add the garlic, ginger, and jalapeño; stir-fry until fragrant, about 1 minute.

2 Add the beef strips and stir-fry until browned, about 3 minutes. Add the scallions and snow peas; stir-fry about 1 minute. Add the broth, soy sauce, sherry, and sugar; bring to a simmer. Reduce the heat and simmer, stirring occasionally, about 2 minutes.

3 Combine the cornstarch and water in a small bowl until smooth. Add the cornstarch mixture to the wok and cook, stirring constantly, until thickened, about 30 seconds.

PER SERVING (1 cup): 140 Cal, 3 g Fat, 1 g Sat Fat, 0 g Trans Fat, 45 mg Chol, 338 mg Sod, 8 g Carb, 2 g Fib, 19 g Prot, 38 mg Calc. **POINTS** value: **3.**

HOW WE DID IT To seed a jalapeño pepper, slice a strip off one side, cutting away about a third of the pepper. Slip your finger or a small spoon into the pepper and gently pull away any membrane and seeds. Do the same with any membrane attached to the section you've cut away. Discard the membrane and seeds.

5 **garlic cloves**, minced

1 tablespoon minced peeled **fresh ginger**

1 **jalapeño**, pepper seeded and minced (wear gloves to prevent irritation)

¾ pound **boneless sirloin steak**, trimmed of visible fat and cut into 2 x ⅛-inch strips

4 **scallions**, cut into 1-inch pieces

2 cups fresh **snow peas**

¼ cup **reduced-sodium chicken broth**

2 tablespoons **reduced-sodium soy sauce**

1 tablespoon **sherry** or **dry vermouth**

1 teaspoon **sugar**

1½ teaspoons **cornstarch**

1 tablespoon cold **water**

Beef Creole

PREP	10 MINUTES
COOK	ABOUT 15 MINUTES
SERVES	4

1 small **onion**, chopped

1 **green bell pepper**, seeded and chopped

1 pound **ground lean beef** (5% or less fat)

1½ teaspoons **dried thyme**

1 (14½-ounce) can **reduced-sodium tomato soup** (not condensed)

¼ cup bottled **chili sauce**

1 (10-ounce) package **frozen cut okra**, thawed

¼ cup chopped **flat-leaf parsley**

4–6 drops **hot pepper sauce**, or to taste

½ teaspoon **salt**

½ teaspoon **filé powder** (optional)

1 Spray a large nonstick saucepan with nonstick spray and set over medium-high heat. Add the onion and bell pepper; cook, stirring occasionally, until softened, about 3 minutes.

2 Add the beef and cook, breaking it apart with a wooden spoon until browned, about 4 minutes. Add the thyme and cook until fragrant, about 20 seconds.

3 Add the tomato soup and chili sauce, stirring to scrape up any browned bits from the bottom of the pan. Stir in the okra and parsley; bring to a simmer. Reduce the heat, cover, and simmer about 8 minutes.

4 Remove the pan from the heat, then stir in the hot pepper sauce, salt, and filé powder, if using.

PER SERVING (1¼ cups): 238 Cal, 7 g Fat, 3 g Sat Fat, 1 g Trans Fat, 64 mg Chol, 759 mg Sod, 18 g Carb, 4 g Fib, 25 g Prot, 95 mg Calc. **POINTS** value: **5.**

DEFINITION *Filé* powder (FEE-lay), a classic Creole ingredient, is actually the ground, dried leaves of the sassafras tree. It has the taste of birch beer. But *filé* isn't just a flavoring; it's also a thickener. It should be stirred into the stew only after the pan is off the heat, as cooking *filé* powder will render it stringy.

Ground Beef and Black-Eyed Pea Stew

PREP	10 MINUTES
COOK	ABOUT 15 MINUTES
SERVES	4

1 small **onion**, chopped

1 pound **ground lean beef** (7% or less fat)

1½ teaspoons **ground allspice**

1 teaspoon **cinnamon**

1 (14½-ounce) **can diced tomatoes**

1 (15-ounce) **can black-eyed peas**, rinsed and drained

¼ cup **currants** or **raisins**

¼ cup chopped **flat-leaf parsley**

¼ teaspoon **salt**

Freshly **ground pepper**

1 Spray a large nonstick saucepan with nonstick spray and set over medium heat. Add the onion and cook, stirring frequently, until translucent, about 3 minutes.

2 Add the beef and cook, breaking it apart with a wooden spoon until browned, about 4 minutes.

3 Add the allspice and cinnamon; cook until fragrant, about 20 seconds. Add the tomatoes, stirring to scrape up any browned bits from the bottom of the pan. Stir in the black-eyed peas and currants; bring to a boil. Reduce the heat and simmer, covered, about 7 minutes.

4 Stir in the parsley, salt, and pepper; simmer, uncovered, about 2 minutes.

PER SERVING (1 cup): 287 Cal, 7 g Fat, 3 g Sat Fat, 0 g Trans Fat, 64 mg Chol, 504 mg Sod, 29 g Carb, 6 g Fib, 29 g Prot, 84 mg Calc. **POINTS** value: **6.**

EXPRESS LANE To save time, you can use frozen chopped onions instead of chopping regular onions. Be aware that as they begin to thaw in the skillet they first give off water before they start to brown.

Spaghetti and Meatballs

PREP	10 MINUTES
COOK	ABOUT 15 MINUTES
SERVES	6

1 Fill a large saucepan with 3 quarts water and bring it to a boil over high heat.

2 Meanwhile, place the pasta sauce and broth in a medium saucepan and set over medium-high heat; bring to a simmer.

3 Combine the beef, bread crumbs, basil, oregano, salt, and pepper in a medium bowl until well mixed. Shape the mixture into 18 meatballs.

4 Slip the meatballs into the simmering pasta sauce. Reduce the heat, cover, and simmer, stirring occasionally, until the meatballs are cooked through, about 12 minutes.

5 When the water boils, add the capellini and cook until tender, about 2 minutes. Drain and rinse under warm water. Serve with the meatballs and sauce.

PER SERVING (1 cup pasta with ½ cup sauce and 3 meatballs): 262 Cal, 5 g Fat, 2 g Sat Fat, 0 g Trans Fat, 42 mg Chol, 676 mg Sod, 35 g Carb, 3 g Fib, 19 g Prot, 37 mg Calc. **POINTS** value: **5.**

GOOD IDEA For the freshest flavor, choose a pasta sauce that's relatively simple, just with herbs or mushrooms—not one with meat or meat flavorings.

3 cups jarred **fat-free pasta sauce**

¼ cup **vegetable broth**

1 pound **ground lean beef** (7% or less fat)

2 tablespoons fresh **whole-wheat bread crumbs** (from ½ slice bread)

2 tablespoons minced **onion of shallot**

1½ teaspoons **dried basil**

1½ teaspoons **dried oregano**

½ teaspoon **salt**

¼ teaspoon freshly **ground pepper**

6 ounces **capellini**

Sweet-and-Sour Veal Cutlets

PREP	10 MINUTES
COOK	ABOUT 15 MINUTES
SERVES	4

4 (¼-pound) **veal scaloppini cutlets**

2 teaspoons mild **paprika**

1 teaspoon **salt**

Freshly **ground pepper**

6 cups shredded **napa cabbage**

1 cup **reduced-sodium vegetable broth**

⅓ cup **raisins**

1½ tablespoons packed **light brown sugar**

1½ tablespoons **cider vinegar**

1 teaspoon **cornstarch**

1 tablespoon cold **water**

1 Sprinkle the veal with the paprika, salt, and pepper. Spray a large nonstick skillet with nonstick spray and set over medium heat. Add 2 of the cutlets and cook until browned, about 1½ minutes on each side. Transfer to a plate and cover lightly with foil to keep warm. Repeat with the other 2 cutlets.

2 Add the cabbage, broth, and raisins to the skillet; stir well. Reduce the heat, cover, and cook until the cabbage is tender, about 7 minutes.

3 Pour any juices that have accumulated around the veal into the skillet; stir in the sugar and vinegar. Increase the heat to medium and simmer, uncovered, about 1 minute.

4 Combine the cornstarch and water in a small bowl until smooth. Add the cornstarch mixture to the skillet and cook, stirring constantly, until thickened, about 30 seconds. Remove pan from heat and slip the cutlets into the sauce.

PER SERVING (1 cutlet and ¾ cup vegetables and sauce): 191 Cal, 4 g Fat, 2 g Sat Fat, 0 g Trans Fat, 74 mg Chol, 973 mg Sod, 19 g Carb, 2 g Fib, 20 g Prot, 145 mg Calc. **POINTS** value: **4.**

GOOD IDEA This comforting dish is delicious with egg noodles (½ cup cooked egg noodles for each serving would increase the **POINTS** value by 2).

Argentina-Style Pork Tenderloin

PREP	15 MINUTES PLUS 2 HOURS CHILLING AND 5 MINUTES STANDING TIME
COOK	ABOUT 20 MINUTES
SERVES	4

1 Place the pork between 2 sheets of wax paper. Pound the pork to ½-inch thickness, using a meat mallet or bottom of a heavy saucepan.

2 To make the marinade, combine the garlic, parsley, lemon juice, oil, rosemary, thyme, and chili powder (if using) in a zip-close plastic bag; add the pork. Squeeze out the air and seal the bag; turn to coat the pork. Refrigerate, turning the bag occasionally, at least 2 hours or overnight.

3 Spray the grill rack with nonstick spray; prepare the grill. Sprinkle the pork with the salt and pepper and place on the grill rack. Grill the pork until an instant-read thermometer inserted into the center registers 160°F, 18–22 minutes. Transfer to a cutting board, cover loosely with foil, and let stand about 5 minutes. Cut into 12 slices.

PER SERVING (3 slices): 159 Cal, 6 g Fat, 2 g Sat Fat, 0 g Trans Fat, 75 mg Chol, 634 mg Sod, 1 g Carb, 0 g Fib, 24 g Prot, 7 mg Calc. *POINTS* value: *4.*

GOOD IDEA Serve this dish with a side of pinto beans (½ cup cooked beans for each serving will increase the *POINTS* value by 2).

☑

1 (1-pound) **pork tenderloin**, trimmed of visible fat

3 **garlic cloves**, minced

3 tablespoons chopped **fresh parsley**

2 tablespoons fresh **lemon juice**

1 tablespoon **extra-virgin olive oil**

1 teaspoon chopped **fresh rosemary**

1 teaspoon chopped **fresh thyme**

⅛ teaspoon **chipotle chili powder** (optional)

1 teaspoon **salt**

¼ teaspoon freshly **ground pepper**

Roast Pork with Root Vegetables

PREP	15 MINUTES PLUS 10 MINUTES STANDING TIME
COOK	45–50 MINUTES
SERVES	8

1 Preheat the oven to 450°F. Spray a large jelly-roll pan with olive oil nonstick spray.

2 Sprinkle the pork roast with ¾ teaspoon of the salt and ¼ teaspoon of the pepper. Rub the Italian seasoning all over the pork roast.

3 Combine the potato, squash, turnips, onion, oil, cinnamon, allspice, and the remaining ¾ teaspoon salt and ¼ teaspoon pepper in a large bowl; toss well. Put the pork in the center of the pan; arrange the vegetable mixture around the pork. Roast, stirring the vegetables once after 30 minutes, until an instant-read thermometer inserted in the center of the pork registers 155°F and the vegetables are browned and tender, 45–50 minutes.

4 Transfer the pork to a cutting board, cover loosely with foil, and let stand 10 minutes (the temperature will increase to 160°F for medium). Cut into 16 slices and serve with the vegetables.

PER SERVING (2 slices pork with ¾ cup vegetables): 227 Cal, 10 g Fat, 3 g Sat Fat, 0 g Trans Fat, 63 mg Chol, 503 mg Sod, 12 g Carb, 3 g Fib, 23 g Prot, 72 mg Calc. **POINTS** value: **5.**

HOW WE DID IT You'll need a large jelly-roll pan for this recipe, approximately 11 x 17 inches, to accommodate all the ingredients.

1 (2-pound) **boneless center-cut pork loin roast**, trimmed of visible fat

1½ teaspoons **salt**

½ teaspoon freshly **ground pepper**

2 tablespoons **Italian seasoning**

1 large **sweet potato**, peeled and cut into 16 pieces

½ **butternut squash**, peeled, seeded, and cut into 16 pieces

2 **turnips**, peeled and cut into 8 wedges each

1 large **onion**, cut into 8 wedges

4 teaspoons **extra-virgin olive oil**

½ teaspoon **cinnamon**

½ teaspoon **ground allspice**

Roast Pork with Root Vegetables

Vietnamese Caramel Pork with Black Pepper

PREP	10 MINUTES
COOK	ABOUT 7 MINUTES
SERVES	4

6 **scallions**, cut into ½-inch pieces

6 **garlic cloves**, minced

1 (1¼-pound) **pork tenderloin**, trimmed of visible fat and cut into 2 x ¼-inch strips

4 teaspoons **sugar**

¼ cup **reduced-sodium chicken broth**

2 tablespoons **Asian fish sauce** (nam pla)

1–2 teaspoons freshly **ground pepper**, or to taste

1 Spray a large nonstick wok or high-sided skillet with nonstick spray and set over high heat. Add the scallions and garlic; stir-fry until softened, about 1 minute. Add the pork and stir-fry until browned, about 3 minutes. Transfer the contents of the wok to a bowl and set aside.

2 Return the wok to the heat and add the sugar; cook, stirring, until melted, lightly browned, and caramelized, about 30 seconds. Slowly stir in the broth. The caramel may form a hard lump. Continue cooking, stirring constantly, until the sugar melts again and the broth boils, about 20 seconds.

3 Stir in the fish sauce and pepper, then return the pork, vegetables, and any accumulated juices in the bowl to the wok. Cook, stirring constantly, until the sauce reduces to a glaze, about 2 minutes. Serve at once.

PER SERVING (¾ cup): 223 Cal, 6 g Fat, 2 g Sat Fat, 0 g Trans Fat, 90 mg Chol, 827 mg Sod, 8 g Carb, 1 g Fib, 33 g Prot, 38 mg Calc. **POINTS** value: **5.**

GOOD IDEA Serve this sweet and fiery ragoût alongside a cooling salad of spring greens, steamed sugar snap peas, and sliced fresh strawberries, sprinkled with red-wine vinegar.

Fajita-Style Skillet Pork

PREP	20 MINUTES
COOK	ABOUT 15 MINUTES
SERVES	4

1 Combine the tomatoes, avocado, cilantro, and lime juice in a medium bowl.

2 Heat 1 teaspoon of the oil in a large nonstick skillet over medium-high heat. Add half the pork and cook, stirring occasionally, until browned and cooked through, about 4 minutes. Transfer the pork to a plate. Repeat with the remaining pork.

3 Heat the remaining 1 teaspoon oil in the same skillet over medium-high heat. Add the onion and bell peppers; cook, stirring occasionally, until the vegetables are very soft, about 5 minutes. Add the pork and Mexican seasoning; cook, stirring frequently, about 1 minute. Stir in the soy sauce and cook until liquid almost evaporates, about 30 seconds. Serve with the salsa.

PER SERVING (1 cup pork mixture with ½ cup salsa): 236 Cal, 10 g Fat, 2 g Sat Fat, 0 g Trans Fat, 63 mg Chol, 403 mg Sod, 13 g Carb, 4 g Fib, 25 g Prot, 20 mg Calc. *POINTS* value: *5.*

☑

1 pint **cherry tomatoes**, quartered

½ medium **avocado**, peeled and cut into ¼-inch cubes

2 tablespoons chopped **fresh cilantro**

1 tablespoon fresh **lime juice**

2 teaspoons **olive oil**

1 pound **pork tenderloin**, trimmed of visible fat and cut into 1 ½ x ¼-inch-thick strips

1 **onion**, sliced

1 **red bell pepper**, seeded and cut into ¼-inch strips

1 **green bell pepper**, seeded and cut into ¼-inch-thick strips

1 teaspoon **Mexican seasoning**

2 tablespoons **reduced-sodium soy sauce**

Teriyaki Pork Stir-Fry

Teriyaki Pork Stir-Fry

PREP	15 MINUTES
COOK	ABOUT 15 MINUTES
SERVES	4

1 Heat a large nonstick skillet or wok over medium-high heat until a drop of water sizzles. Pour in 2 teaspoons of the oil and swirl to coat the pan, then add half the pork. Stir-fry until browned and cooked through, about 4 minutes. Transfer the pork to a plate with a slotted spoon. Repeat with the remaining pork.

2 Heat the remaining 2 teaspoons oil in the same skillet over medium-high heat. Add the mushrooms and stir-fry until they begin to soften, about 1 minute. Add the bell pepper, ginger, and garlic; stir-fry until slightly softened, about 2 minutes. Add the pork and snow peas; stir-fry until the snow peas turn bright green, about 1 minute. Add the broth, teriyaki sauce, and orange zest; cook until the sauce thickens slightly and the vegetables are crisp-tender, about 1 minute.

PER SERVING (1 cup): 218 Cal, 9 g Fat, 2 g Sat Fat, 0 g Trans Fat, 63 mg Chol, 332 mg Sod, 9 g Carb, 2 g Fib, 25 g Prot, 23 mg Calc. **POINTS** value: **5.**

EXPRESS LANE To cut down on the prep time, instead of cutting mushrooms, bell pepper, and snow peas as the recipe directs, just toss in your favorite pre-cut veggies from the salad bar.

4 teaspoons **sunflower oil**

1 pound **pork tenderloin**, trimmed of visible fat and cut into 1 x ¼-inch-thick strips

¼ pound **fresh shiitake mushrooms**, stems removed and sliced

1 **red bell pepper**, seeded and cut into thin strips

1 tablespoon grated peeled **fresh ginger**

2 **garlic cloves**, minced

¼ pound **fresh snow peas**, trimmed and halved lengthwise

¼ cup **reduced-sodium chicken broth**

3 tablespoons **reduced-sodium teriyaki sauce**

1 teaspoon grated **orange zest**

White Chili

PREP	10 MINUTES
COOK	ABOUT 15 MINUTES
SERVES	4

1 Spray a large nonstick saucepan with nonstick spray and set over medium-high heat. Add the onion, bell pepper, and garlic; cook, stirring, until softened, about 2 minutes. Add the pork and cook, stirring, until browned, about 3 minutes.

2 Stir in the beans, broth, chiles, cumin, oregano, and hot pepper sauce. Bring to a boil. Simmer uncovered, stirring occasionally, until the pork is cooked through and the flavors are blended, about 10 minutes. Season with the salt and pepper. Serve, topped with the cheese.

PER SERVING (1 cup with 1 tablespoon cheese): 260 Cal, 4 g Fat, 1 g Sat Fat, 0 g Trans Fat, 55 mg Chol, 455 mg Sod, 26 g Carb, 6 g Fib, 30 g Prot, 157 mg Calc. *POINTS* value: *5.*

GOOD IDEA If you wish, serve the chili with chopped fresh tomatoes and brown rice (½ cup cooked brown rice will increase the *POINTS* value by 2).

1 **onion**, chopped

1 **green bell pepper**, seeded and chopped

2 **garlic cloves**, minced

¾ pound **pork tenderloin**, trimmed of visible fat and cut into ¼-inch cubes

1 (15-ounce) **can white beans**, rinsed and drained

1½ cups **reduced-sodium chicken broth**

1 (4½-ounce) can chopped **mild green chiles**

1 teaspoon **ground cumin**

1 teaspoon **dried oregano**

2–4 dashes **hot pepper sauce**, or to taste

½ teaspoon **salt**

Freshly **ground pepper**

¼ cup shredded **fat-free cheddar cheese**

Pork and Bean Chili

PREP	15 MINUTES
COOK	ABOUT 25 MINUTES
SERVES	6

1 Heat 2 teaspoons of the oil in a large nonstick saucepan over medium-high heat. Add the pork and cook, stirring occasionally, until browned, about 4 minutes. Transfer the pork to a plate.

2 Heat the remaining 2 teaspoons of oil in the same saucepan over medium-high heat. Add the onion, bell pepper, and garlic; cook, stirring occasionally, until slightly softened, about 3 minutes. Stir in the tomatoes and their juice, the chili powder, cumin, oregano, salt, and pepper; cook until the mixture comes to a boil, about 4 minutes. Stir in the beans; reduce the heat and simmer, covered, until the mixture thickens slightly, about 7 minutes. Add the pork and cook until the pork is cooked through, about 5 minutes.

PER SERVING (about ⅔ cup): 188 Cal, 6 g Fat, 1 g Sat Fat, 0 g Trans Fat, 42 mg Chol, 415 mg Sod, 14 g Carb, 4 g Fib, 19 g Prot, 55 mg Calc. **POINTS** value: **3.**

EXPRESS LANE Chili is one of those dishes whose flavor benefits by being prepared ahead, so make it the night before or double the amount for another meal later in the week. The recipe can be refrigerated up to 2 days or frozen up to 1 month.

4 teaspoons **canola oil**

1 pound **pork tenderloin**, trimmed of visible fat and cut into 1-inch cubes

1 **onion**, chopped

1 **green bell pepper**, seeded and chopped

2 **garlic cloves**, minced

1 (14¾-ounce) **can whole peeled tomatoes**, chopped

2 teaspoons **chili powder**

1 teaspoon **ground cumin**

1 teaspoon **dried oregano**

½ teaspoon **salt**

¼ teaspoon freshly **ground pepper**

1 (15½-ounce) **can pinto beans**, rinsed and drained

Pork Chops with Pear Sauce

PREP	10 MINUTES
COOK	ABOUT 15 MINUTES
SERVES	4

1 Heat 1 teaspoon of the oil in a small saucepan over medium heat. Add the pears, ½ teaspoon of the cinnamon, and the nutmeg; cook, stirring frequently and mashing the pears with a spoon, until thick and the pears are tender, about 4 minutes. Remove the pan from the heat; stir in the lemon zest and vanilla. Set aside.

2 Combine the remaining ¼ teaspoon cinnamon, the salt, paprika, and pepper in a bowl. Rub the mixture over the pork. Heat the remaining 1 teaspoon oil in a medium nonstick skillet over medium-high heat. Add the pork and cook until well browned and cooked through, about 4 minutes on each side. Serve with the sauce.

PER SERVING (1 pork chop with 3 tablespoons sauce): 221 Cal, 9 g Fat, 3 g Sat Fat, 0 g Trans Fat, 67 mg Chol, 488 mg Sod, 11 g Carb, 2 g Fib, 24 g Prot, 32 mg Calc. **POINTS** value: **5.**

FOOD NOTE When buying pears for this dish, select fruit that yield lightly to pressure and are very fragrant. Good varieties for this recipe include Bartlett, Anjou, or Bosc.

2 teaspoons **canola oil**

2 ripe **pears**, peeled and chopped

¾ teaspoon **cinnamon**

⅛ teaspoon ground **nutmeg**

1 teaspoon grated **lemon zest**

½ teaspoon **vanilla extract**

¾ teaspoon **salt**

½ teaspoon **paprika**

¼ teaspoon freshly **ground pepper**

4 (¼-pound) **boneless center-cut pork loin chops**, ½ inch thick, trimmed of visible fat

Bistro Pork Sauté

PREP	10 MINUTES
COOK	ABOUT 15 MINUTES
SERVES	4

1 Spray a large nonstick skillet with nonstick spray and set over medium-high heat. Season the pork chops with the salt and pepper, then place in the skillet and cook until browned, 1–2 minutes on each side. Transfer the chops to a plate.

2 Add the Brussels sprouts and broth to the skillet; bring to a boil, scraping up any browned bits from the bottom of the pan. Stir in the Worcestershire sauce, mustard, and allspice.

3 Return the pork and any accumulated juices to the skillet. Reduce the heat, cover, and simmer until the pork is cooked through, about 12 minutes.

4 Transfer the pork chops to 4 plates. Raise the heat to high and boil the sauce until slightly thickened, about 2 minutes. Spoon the sauce over the chops.

PER SERVING (1 chop with ¾ cup Brussels sprouts and sauce): 284 Cal, 11 g Fat, 4 g Sat Fat, 0 g Trans Fat, 87 mg Chol, 672 mg Sod, 11 g Carb, 5 g Fib, 35 g Prot, 50 mg Calc. **POINTS** value: **6.**

GOOD IDEA Choose small sprouts if possible; they tend to be less bitter.

4 (5-ounce) **boneless pork loin chops**, about ½ inch thick, trimmed of visible fat

½ teaspoon **salt**

Freshly **ground pepper**

1 pound fresh **Brussels sprouts**, trimmed and thinly sliced

1¼ cups **reduced-sodium chicken broth**

1 tablespoon **white wine Worcestershire sauce** or Worcestershire sauce for chicken

1 tablespoon **Dijon mustard**

½ teaspoon ground **allspice**

Pork Cutlets with Apples and Leeks

PREP	10 MINUTES
COOK	ABOUT 15 MINUTES
SERVES	4

1 Place the pork chops between sheets of wax paper. Pound them to ½-inch thickness using the smooth side of a meat mallet or the bottom of a heavy, large saucepan. Season the chops with salt and pepper.

2 Spray a large nonstick skillet with nonstick spray and set over medium-high heat. Add the pork; cook until browned, about 1 minute on each side. Transfer the chops to a plate.

3 Melt the butter in the skillet; add the leeks and apples. Cook, stirring, until softened, about 2 minutes. Stir in the broth, scraping up any browned bits from the bottom of the pan. Stir in the caraway seeds and nutmeg.

4 Return the chops and any accumulated juices to the skillet; bring to a simmer. Reduce the heat, cover, and simmer until the chops are cooked through, about 10 minutes.

5 Transfer the chops to a platter. Combine the cornstarch and water in a small bowl until smooth. Add the cornstarch mixture to the skillet and cook, stirring constantly, until thickened, about 30 seconds. Pour sauce over the chops.

PER SERVING (1 chop with ½ cup vegetables and sauce): 268 Cal, 11 g Fat, 4 g Sat Fat, 0 g Trans Fat, 75 mg Chol, 415 mg Sod, 17 g Carb, 2 g Fib, 26 g Prot, 42 mg Calc. **POINTS** value: **6.**

HOW WE DID IT Leeks can be very sandy—here's an easy way to clean them: Split them in half the long way, keeping them together by leaving the root intact. Then wash them carefully under running water, making sure you get between the layers to remove any grit.

4 (¼-pound) **boneless pork loin chops**, trimmed of visible fat

½ teaspoon **salt**

Freshly **ground pepper**

2 teaspoons **unsalted butter**

2 large **leeks**, cleaned and thinly sliced (white and light green parts only)

2 **tart apples**, such as Granny Smith or McIntosh, peeled, cored, and thinly sliced

½ cup **reduced-sodium chicken broth**

1 teaspoon **caraway seeds**

¼ teaspoon grated **nutmeg**

1 teaspoon **cornstarch**

2 teaspoons cold **water**

Pork Cutlets with
Apples and Leeks

Barbecued Pressure-Cooker Pork

PREP	10 MINUTES
COOK	ABOUT 15 MINUTES
SERVES	4

1 small **onion**, chopped

1 **green bell pepper**, seeded and chopped

¾ pound **ground lean pork**

1 large **sweet potato** (12 ounces), peeled and shredded

1 cup bottled **barbecue sauce**

1 Spray a large pressure cooker with nonstick spray and set over medium-high heat. Add the onion and bell pepper; cook, stirring, until softened, about 2 minutes.

2 Add the pork and cook, breaking it apart with a wooden spoon, until lightly browned, about 1 minute. Add the sweet potato, barbecue sauce, and broth. Lock the lid in place and raise the heat to high. Bring the cooker to high pressure, following the manufacturer's directions. Reduce the heat and cook at high pressure for 10 minutes.

3 Place the pot in the sink and run cold water over it to bring the pressure down quickly. When the pressure indicator releases, remove the pot from the sink and unlock the lid, following the manufacturer's directions. Stir the stew well before serving.

PER SERVING (1 cup): 309 Cal, 7 g Fat, 2 g Sat Fat, 0 g Trans Fat, 54 mg Chol, 709 mg Sod, 42 g Carb, 3 g Fib, 21 g Prot, 51 mg Calc. **POINTS** value: **6.**

GOOD IDEA You can eat this stew on its own, wrap it in lettuce leaves for a taste of Thai, or serve it in hamburger buns (a 1-ounce bun for each serving will increase the **POINTS** value by 2). Choose a sweet barbecue sauce, or if you prefer a Texas barbecue flavor, a vinegar-based sauce.

Ham and Egg Frittata

PREP	10 MINUTES PLUS 5 MINUTES STANDING TIME
COOK	ABOUT 20 MINUTES
SERVES	4

1 Heat the oil in a medium ovenproof skillet (such as cast iron or stainless steel) with an ovenproof handle over medium heat. Add the onion and mushrooms; cook until the mushrooms give off their liquid and the onion slightly softens, about 2 minutes. Add the ham and basil; cook, stirring occasionally, until the onion and ham are lightly browned, about 7 minutes. Add the tomatoes and cook, stirring occasionally, until heated through, about 2 minutes.

2 Preheat the broiler. Lightly beat the eggs, egg whites, and pepper in a small bowl; pour over the ham mixture, stirring gently to combine. Sprinkle with the cheese. Cook, without stirring, until the eggs are set, about 7 minutes. Place the frittata in the skillet under the broiler and broil until the top is lightly browned, about 2 minutes. Let the frittata stand 5 minutes before serving.

PER SERVING (¼ of frittata): 207 Cal, 9 g Fat, 2 g Sat Fat, 0 g Trans Fat, 185 mg Chol, 1,023 mg Sod, 8 g Carb, 1 g Fib, 24 g Prot, 111 mg Calc.
POINTS value: **5.**

GOOD IDEA If your skillet doesn't have an ovenproof handle, simply wrap it in a double layer of foil before placing the skillet under the broiler.

2 teaspoons **extra-virgin olive oil**

1 **onion**, chopped

5 fresh **white mushrooms**, sliced

1 (½-pound) **boneless ham steak**, cut into ¼-inch pieces

½ teaspoon **dried basil**

½ cup **grape tomatoes**, halved

3 large **eggs**

3 **egg whites**

¼ teaspoon freshly **ground pepper**

3 (¾-ounce) slices **fat-free Swiss cheese**, chopped

Chinese Sour Green Beans and Minced Pork

PREP	10 MINUTES PLUS 5 MINUTES STANDING TIME
COOK	ABOUT 5 MINUTES
SERVES	4

1 Bring the vinegar and water to a rolling boil in a medium saucepan over high heat. Add the beans, cover, and turn off the heat. Set aside 5 minutes; drain.

2 Spray a large nonstick wok or high-sided skillet with nonstick spray and set over high heat until a drop of water sizzles. Add the scallions, garlic, and ginger; stir-fry until softened, about 2 minutes. Add the pork and stir-fry, breaking it apart with a wooden spoon, until browned and cooked through, about 4 minutes.

3 Add the soy sauce and crushed red pepper, stir well, then add the beans. Cook, stirring, until heated through, about 1 minute.

PER SERVING (1 cup): 196 Cal, 7 g Fat, 2 g Sat Fat, 0 g Trans Fat, 54 mg Chol, 465 mg Sod, 12 g Carb, 4 g Fib, 22 g Prot, 81 mg Calc. **POINTS** value: **4.**

GOOD IDEA Steamed bok choy, tossed with a little reduced-sodium soy sauce and a splash of white balsamic vinegar would make a tasty accompaniment to this Szechuan-style stir-fry.

2 cups **white distilled vinegar**

1 cup **water**

1 pound fresh **green beans**, cut into ¼-inch pieces

6 **scallions**, thinly sliced

3 **garlic cloves**, minced

2 tablespoons minced peeled **fresh ginger**

¾ pound **ground lean pork**

3 tablespoons **reduced-sodium soy sauce**

½ teaspoon **crushed red pepper**

Pork, Salsa, and Hominy Soup

PREP	10 MINUTES
COOK	30 MINUTES
SERVES	4

1 Heat a nonstick Dutch oven over medium-high heat. Add the pork and onion; cook, stirring frequently to break up the pork, until browned, about 5 minutes.

2 Add the broth, hominy, salsa, garlic, cumin, and oregano; bring to a boil. Reduce the heat and simmer, covered, until the flavors are blended, about 15 minutes.

3 Stirring constantly, gradually add the cornmeal to the soup. Cook, stirring occasionally, until slightly thickened, about 5 minutes. Remove the Dutch oven from the heat and stir in the cilantro.

PER SERVING (1¼ cups): 167 Cal, 3 g Fat, 1 g Sat Fat, 0 g Trans Fat, 32 mg Chol, 774 mg Sod, 19 g Carb, 3 g Fib, 15 g Prot, 35 mg Calc.
POINTS value: **3.**

½ pound **ground lean pork**

1 **onion**, chopped

2 cups **reduced-sodium chicken broth**

1 (15-ounce) can **golden hominy**, drained

1 cup **fat-free green salsa**

2 **garlic cloves**, minced

½ teaspoon **ground cumin**

½ teaspoon **dried oregano**

1 tablespoon **cornmeal**

⅓ cup chopped **fresh cilantro**

Microwaved Pork and Beans

PREP	5 MINUTES PLUS 3 MINUTES STANDING TIME
COOK	12 MINUTES
SERVES	6

1 Stir all the ingredients together in an 8-cup microwavable baking dish.

2 Microwave on High for 12 minutes, stirring every 3 minutes, until bubbling. Let stand about 3 minutes before serving.

PER SERVING (scant 1 cup): 247 Cal, 4 g Fat, 1 g Sat Fat, 0 g Trans Fat, 18 mg Chol, 1230 mg Sod, 39 g Carb, 10 g Fib, 17 g Prot, 81 mg Calc. *POINTS* value: **4.**

PLAY IT SAFE If you're transporting this, put it in an insulated container until ready to eat. Keep the temperature above 140°F. Standard-size casserole dishes are available to purchase with insulated carrying bags with a pack that you can either freeze or heat to maintain the food at a safe temperature.

½ pound **Canadian bacon**, minced

2 (15-ounce) cans **pinto beans**, rinsed and drained

1 (15-ounce) **can tomato sauce**

1 **green bell pepper**, seeded and chopped

2 tablespoons **dehydrated** minced **onion**

2 tablespoons packed **light brown sugar**

2 tablespoons **cider vinegar**

1 tablespoon **yellow mustard**

1 tablespoon **mild paprika**

2 teaspoons **liquid smoke** (optional)

1 teaspoon **ground cumin**

½ teaspoon **celery seed**

¼ teaspoon **garlic powder**

2–3 dashes **hot pepper sauce**, or to taste

Freshly **ground pepper**

Lamb Stew with Potatoes, Parsnips, and Carrots

PREP	15 MINUTES
COOK	ABOUT 1 HOUR 10 MINUTES
SERVES	6

1 Heat 2 teaspoons of the oil in a nonstick Dutch oven over medium-high heat. Add half the lamb and cook, turning frequently, until browned, about 4 minutes. Transfer the lamb to a plate. Repeat with the remaining lamb.

2 Heat the remaining 2 teaspoons oil over in the same Dutch oven medium-high heat. Add the onions, carrots, parsnip, garlic, and thyme; cook, stirring occasionally, until the onions thaw and the other vegetables slightly soften, about 3 minutes. Stir in the broth, potatoes, and lamb; bring to a boil. Reduce the heat and simmer, covered, until the lamb is tender, about 50 minutes. Stir in the salt and pepper.

PER SERVING (1 cup): 292 Cal, 9 g Fat, 3 g Sat Fat, 0 g Trans Fat, 65 mg Chol, 395 mg Sod, 28 g Carb, 3 g Fib, 25 g Prot, 40 mg Calc. **POINTS** value: **6.**

4 teaspoons **extra-virgin olive oil**

1½ pounds **boneless leg of lamb**, trimmed of visible fat and cut into 1-inch cubes

1 cup frozen **small white onions**

1 cup **baby carrots**

1 large **parsnip**, peeled and cut into 1-inch pieces

3 **garlic cloves**, minced

2 teaspoons chopped **fresh thyme**, or ½ teaspoon dried

1 (14½-ounce) can **reduced-sodium beef broth**

1 pound **red potatoes**, cut into 1-inch pieces

½ teaspoon **salt**

¼ teaspoon freshly **ground pepper**

Couscous-Stuffed
Leg of Lamb

Couscous-Stuffed Leg of Lamb

PREP	20 MINUTES PLUS 2 HOURS CHILLING AND 15 MINUTES STANDING TIME
COOK	60–70 MINUTES
SERVES	8

1 Rub the lamb with the garlic and oil. Transfer to a bowl; cover and refrigerate 2 hours.

2 Meanwhile, bring the water to a boil in a small saucepan. Stir in the couscous; remove the saucepan from the heat. Let stand 5 minutes; fluff with a fork. Transfer the couscous to a bowl. Stir in the basil, chives, mustard, parsley, lemon zest, and ¼ teaspoon of the salt. Cover and refrigerate the stuffing until ready to use.

3 Preheat the oven to 400°F. Arrange the lamb, boned-side up, on a work surface. Sprinkle with the remaining 1¼ teaspoons salt and the pepper. Spread the couscous stuffing onto the lamb. Starting from a longer side, roll up the lamb to enclose the filling. Tie the lamb securely at 2-inch intervals with kitchen string.

4 Spray a wire rack with canola nonstick spray and put in a large roasting pan. Put the lamb on the rack. Roast the lamb until an instant-read thermometer inserted into the thickest part of the lamb registers 145°F for medium-rare, 60–70 minutes. Transfer to a cutting board, cover loosely with foil, and let stand about 10 minutes. Remove the string and cut into 16 slices.

PER SERVING (2 slices lamb with 3 tablespoons stuffing): 249 Cal, 9 g Fat, 3 g Sat Fat, 0 g Trans Fat, 81 mg Chol, 593 mg Sod, 12 g Carb, 2 g Fib, 28 g Prot, 25 mg Calc. **POINTS** value: **5.**

HOW WE DID IT Prepping the lamb is a breeze if you ask the butcher to butterfly and trim it for you. Be sure to trim away any extra fat when you get it home. When you roll it up, don't worry if a little stuffing falls out, just gently pack it back into either end of the roll.

---

1 (2½-pound) butterflied **leg of lamb**, trimmed of visible fat

3 **garlic cloves**, minced

1 tablespoon **extra-virgin olive oil**

¾ cup **water**

½ cup **whole-wheat couscous**

¼ cup chopped **fresh basil**

2 tablespoons chopped **fresh chives**

2 tablespoons **Dijon mustard**

1 tablespoon chopped **fresh parsley**

2 teaspoons grated **lemon zest**

1½ teaspoons **salt**

½ teaspoon freshly **ground pepper**

Hunan Lamb

PREP	10 MINUTES PLUS 2 MINUTES STANDING TIME
COOK	ABOUT 5 MINUTES
SERVES	4

1 Spray a large nonstick wok or high-sided skillet with nonstick spray and set over high heat until a drop of water sizzles. Add the scallions, ginger, and garlic; stir-fry just until fragrant, about 10 seconds.

2 Add the lamb and stir-fry until browned, about 2 minutes. Add the bell pepper strips and stir-fry, about 2 minutes. Stir in the hoisin sauce, soy sauce, vinegar, chile sauce, and sesame oil; cook, stirring, until fragrant, about 1 minute.

3 Combine the cornstarch and water in a small bowl until smooth. Add the cornstarch mixture to the wok and cook, stirring constantly, until thickened, about 30 seconds. Remove the wok from the heat and let the stir-fry stand 2 minutes before serving.

PER SERVING (1¼ cups): 200 Cal, 8 g Fat, 2 g Sat Fat, 0 g Trans Fat, 62 mg Chol, 271 mg Sod, 12 g Carb, 3 g Fib, 21 g Prot, 37 mg Calc. **POINTS** value: **4.**

GOOD IDEA Serve this dish over brown rice (½ cup per serving will increase the **POINTS** value by 2) or steamed shredded Chinese cabbage.

6 **scallions**, thinly sliced

1 tablespoon minced peeled **fresh ginger**

2 **garlic cloves**, minced

¾ pound **lamb loin**, trimmed of visible fat and cut into ¼-inch-thick strips

3 assorted color **bell peppers**, seeded and thinly sliced

1 tablespoon **hoisin sauce**

1 tablespoon **reduced-sodium soy sauce**

1 tablespoon **rice vinegar**

1 teaspoon bottled **Asian red chile sauce**, or to taste

1 teaspoon **Asian** (dark) **sesame oil**

1 teaspoon **cornstarch**

2 teaspoons cold **water**

Lamb Chops with Roasted Garlic Aïoli

PREP	15 MINUTES PLUS 5 MINUTES COOLING TIME
COOK	ABOUT 18 MINUTES
SERVES	4

½ teaspoon **extra-virgin olive oil**

4 small **garlic cloves**, unpeeled

¼ cup **fat-free mayonnaise**

½ teaspoon grated **lemon zest**

4 (5-ounce) **loin lamb chops**, about 1 inch thick, trimmed of visible fat

¼ teaspoon **salt**

⅛ teaspoon freshly **ground pepper**

1 Spray the grill rack with nonstick spray; prepare the grill.

2 To make the aïoli, combine the oil and garlic in a small nonstick skillet. Cook over medium-low heat, shaking the pan and turning the garlic occasionally, until golden and softened, 8–10 minutes. Transfer to a small bowl; cool about 5 minutes. Peel the garlic and mash in a bowl with a wooden spoon. Stir in the mayonnaise and lemon zest.

3 Sprinkle the lamb with the salt and pepper and place on the grill rack. Grill the lamb until an instant-read thermometer inserted in the center of each chop registers 145°F for medium-rare, about 4 minutes on each side. Serve the chops with the aïoli.

PER SERVING (1 chop with about 1 tablespoon aïoli): 150 Cal, 7 g Fat, 2 g Sat Fat, 0 g Trans Fat, 58 mg Chol, 316 mg Sod, 3 g Carb, 0 g Fib, 18 g Prot, 18 mg Calc. **POINTS** value: **4.**

GOOD IDEA *Aïoli* (ay-OH-lee) is a garlic-flavored mayonnaise from France. Our healthy version is also terrific with poultry, fish, and vegetables, so double the *aïoli,* prepare as directed in Step 2, and refrigerate until ready to use, up to 1 week.

Spiced Lamb Chops with Cucumber and Red Onion Salad

PREP	10 MINUTES
COOK	ABOUT 10 MINUTES
SERVES	4

1 Spray the grill rack with nonstick spray; prepare the grill.

2 Combine the cucumbers, onion, vinegar, cilantro, ½ teaspoon of the salt, and ⅛ teaspoon of the pepper in a medium bowl.

3 Combine the cumin, paprika, chili powder, and the remaining ¼ teaspoon salt and ⅛ teaspoon pepper in a small bowl. Rub the spice mixture over both sides of the lamb.

4 Place the lamb on the grill rack. Grill the lamb until an instant-read thermometer inserted in the center of each chop registers 145°F for medium-rare, about 4 minutes on each side. Serve with the cucumber and red onion salad.

PER SERVING (1 chop with ¾ cup salad): 147 Cal, 6 g Fat, 2 g Sat Fat, 0 g Trans Fat, 57 mg Chol, 491 mg Sod, 4 g Carb, 1 g Fib, 19 g Prot, 31 mg Calc. **POINTS** value: **3.**

GOOD IDEA If you want to dress up this dish, serve with a side of wild and brown rice (⅔ cup cooked rice for each serving with increase the **POINTS** value by 2).

2 medium **cucumbers**, peeled, halved lengthwise, and thinly sliced

1 small **red onion**, thinly sliced

1 tablespoon **cider vinegar**

1 tablespoon chopped **fresh cilantro**

¾ teaspoon **salt**

¼ teaspoon freshly **ground pepper**

½ teaspoon **ground cumin**

½ teaspoon **paprika**

¼ teaspoon **chili powder**

4 (5-ounce) **loin lamb chops**, about 1 inch thick, trimmed of visible fat

Spiced Lamb Chops with Cucumber
and Red Onion Salad

Lamb Chops with Mango-Mint Salsa

PREP	15 MINUTES
COOK	ABOUT 10 MINUTES
SERVES	4

1 Spray the grill rack with nonstick spray; prepare the grill.

2 To make the salsa, combine the mango, onion, mint, lemon juice, and ¼ teaspoon of the salt in a small bowl.

3 Combine the basil, coriander, fennel, cayenne, and the remaining ½ teaspoon salt in another small bowl. Rub the spice mixture over both sides of the lamb.

4 Place the lamb on the grill rack. Grill the lamb until an instant-read thermometer inserted in the center of each chop registers 145°F for medium-rare, about 5 minutes on each side. Serve with the salsa.

PER SERVING (1 chop with 6 tablespoons salsa): 174 Cal, 6 g Fat, 2 g Sat Fat, 0 g Trans Fat, 57 mg Chol, 488 mg Sod, 11 g Carb, 1 g Fib, 18 g Prot, 34 mg Calc. **POINTS** value: **4.**

HOW WE DID IT When it comes to selecting a ripe mango, let your nose be your guide. Choose a mango that smells fragrant and sweet; the fruit should also yield slightly to the touch.

1 medium **mango**, peeled, pitted, and diced

½ small **red onion**, finely chopped

2 tablespoons chopped **fresh mint**

1 tablespoon fresh **lemon juice**

¾ teaspoon **salt**

1 teaspoon **dried basil**

¾ teaspoon **ground coriander**

¾ teaspoon **fennel seeds**, crushed

⅛ teaspoon **cayenne**

4 (5-ounce) **loin lamb chops**, about 1 inch thick, trimmed of visible fat

Ground Lamb Kebabs with Couscous

PREP	10 MINUTES PLUS 5 MINUTES STANDING TIME
COOK	ABOUT 10 MINUTES
SERVES	4

1 Spray the broiler pan with nonstick spray and preheat the broiler.

2 Mix the lamb, dill, oil, onion, garlic, oregano, cumin, salt, and pepper in a medium bowl. Form into 8 balls. Thread the balls onto 4 metal skewers.

3 Broil the kebabs 5 inches from the heat, turning once, until cooked through, about 10 minutes.

4 Meanwhile, heat the broth to a boil in a small saucepan. Mix the couscous, currants, and parsley in a medium bowl. Pour the boiling broth over the couscous, stir well, cover and set aside until the couscous absorbs all the liquid, about 5 minutes. Fluff the couscous with a fork and divide among 4 plates. Top each mound of couscous with a skewer of lamb kebabs.

PER SERVING (1 skewer and ¾ cup couscous): 420 Cal, 12 g Fat, 3 g Sat Fat, 1 g Trans Fat, 82 mg Chol, 645 mg Sod, 43 g Carb, 3 g Fib, 33 g Prot, 60 mg Calc. **POINTS** value: **9.**

1 pound **ground lean lamb**

¼ cup chopped **fresh dill**, or 2 tablespoons dried

1 tablespoon **olive oil**

1 tablespoon minced **onion** or **shallot**

1 **garlic clove**, minced

1 tablespoon fresh **oregano leaves**, chopped, or 2 teaspoons dried

1 teaspoon **ground cumin**

½ teaspoon **salt**

Freshly **ground pepper**

2 cups **reduced-sodium chicken broth**

1 cup **couscous**

¼ cup **dried currants** or **raisins**

¼ cup packed fresh **flat-leaf parsley** leaves, chopped

CHAPTER 5

Chicken and Turkey Favorites

Herb-Roasted Chicken

Herb-Roasted Chicken

PREP	10 MINUTES PLUS 10 MINUTES STANDING TIME
COOK	1¼–1½ HOURS
SERVES	6

1 Preheat the oven to 375°F. Combine the basil, parsley, oregano, rosemary, oil, salt, and pepper in a bowl.

2 Rinse the chicken inside and out; pat dry with paper towels. Carefully lift the skin from the chicken breast and thighs and rub the herb mixture evenly outside the chicken, under the skin, and in the cavity. Place the rack of a roasting pan in the pan; spray with canola nonstick spray. Place the chicken, breast-side up, on the rack. Place the garlic in the chicken cavity.

3 Roast the chicken, basting occasionally with the pan juices, until an instant-read thermometer inserted into the thigh registers 180°F, 1¼–1½ hours. Transfer the chicken to a cutting board. Let stand about 10 minutes before carving. Remove the skin before eating.

PER SERVING (⅙ of chicken): 212 Cal, 9 g Fat, 2 g Sat Fat, 0 g Trans Fat, 90 mg Chol, 379 mg Sod, 1 g Carb, 0 g Fib, 30 g Prot, 27 mg Calc. **POINTS** value: **5.**

GOOD IDEA For a citrus touch, prick 1 lemon in several places with a fork and place in the cavity of the chicken along with the garlic.

2 tablespoons chopped **fresh basil**

2 tablespoons chopped **fresh parsley**

1 tablespoon chopped **fresh oregano**

1 teaspoon chopped **fresh rosemary**, or ½ teaspoon dried

2 teaspoons **extra-virgin olive oil**

¾ teaspoon **salt**

¼ teaspoon freshly **ground pepper**

1 (3½-pound) **chicken**, giblets discarded

5 **garlic cloves**, peeled

Tarragon Chicken with 40 Cloves of Garlic

PREP	10 MINUTES PLUS 10 MINUTES STANDING TIME
COOK	ABOUT 1 HOUR 20 MINUTES
SERVES	8

3 tablespoons chopped **fresh tarragon**

1 teaspoon **salt**

½ teaspoon freshly **ground pepper**

1 (3½-pound) **chicken**, giblets discarded

40 **garlic cloves**, unpeeled

1 cup **reduced-sodium chicken broth**

1 Preheat the oven to 400°F. Spray a shallow roasting pan with olive oil nonstick spray.

2 Combine the tarragon, salt, and pepper in a small bowl. Lightly spray the herb mixture with olive oil nonstick spray; stir to combine.

3 Carefully lift the skin from the chicken breast, thighs, and legs; spread the herb mixture evenly under the skin. Tuck the wings behind the chicken. If desired, tie the legs closed with kitchen string to help hold the shape of the bird during roasting. Place the chicken, breast-side up, in the pan.

4 Arrange the garlic cloves around the chicken; pour the broth into the pan. Roast the chicken until an instant-read thermometer inserted into the thigh registers 180°F and the garlic cloves are soft, about 1 hour 20 minutes. Transfer the chicken to a cutting board. Let stand about 10 minutes before carving. Remove the skin before eating. Serve the chicken with the garlic cloves.

PER SERVING (⅛ of chicken with 5 garlic cloves): 172 Cal, 6 g Fat, 2 g Sat Fat, 0 g Trans Fat, 68 mg Chol, 436 mg Sod, 5 g Carb, 0 g Fib, 23 g Prot, 43 mg Calc. **POINTS** value: **4.**

HOW WE DID IT To serve the roasted garlic in this dish, gently squeeze the softened garlic from each clove and spread over the carved chicken. Its sweet and mellow flavor is delicious!

Citrus Chicken Breasts

PREP	15 MINUTES PLUS 1 HOUR CHILLING TIME
COOK	ABOUT 35 MINUTES
SERVES	4

1 To make the marinade, combine half the garlic, the soy sauce, ginger, 1 teaspoon of the lemon zest, ½ teaspoon of the orange zest, and the fennel in a medium bowl. Add the chicken and toss well to coat. Cover and refrigerate 1 hour.

2 Preheat the oven to 450°F. Spray a roasting pan with olive oil nonstick spray. Remove the chicken from the marinade; sprinkle with ¼ teaspoon of the salt and ⅛ teaspoon of the pepper. Heat 2 teaspoons of the oil in a large nonstick skillet over medium-high heat. Add the chicken, skinned-side down, and cook until well browned, about 4 minutes. Turn the chicken and cook 2 minutes longer. Transfer the chicken to the roasting pan. Bake until an instant-read thermometer inserted into a breast registers 170°F, 20–23 minutes.

3 Meanwhile, heat the remaining 2 teaspoons oil in the same skillet over medium heat. Add the remaining garlic and the shallot; cook, stirring frequently, until fragrant, about 30 seconds. Stir in the broth and lemon juice; bring to a boil. Cook until the mixture is reduced to ¾ cup, about 4 minutes. Remove the skillet from the heat. Stir in the remaining 1½ teaspoons orange zest, 1 teaspoon lemon zest, ¼ teaspoon salt, ⅛ teaspoon pepper, and the basil. Serve the chicken with the sauce.

PER SERVING (1 chicken breast half with 3 tablespoons sauce): 155 Cal, 7 g Fat, 1 g Sat Fat, 0 g Trans Fat, 51 mg Chol, 605 mg Sod, 3 g Carb, 0 g Fib, 20 g Prot, 19 mg Calc. **POINTS** value: **4.**

4 **garlic cloves**, minced

3 tablespoons reduced-sodium **soy sauce**

1 tablespoon minced peeled **fresh ginger**

2 teaspoons grated **lemon zest**

2 teaspoons grated **orange zest**

½ teaspoon ground **fennel**

4 (¼-pound) bone-in **chicken breast** halves, skinned

½ teaspoon **salt**

¼ teaspoon freshly **ground pepper**

4 teaspoons **extra-virgin olive oil**

1 small **shallot**, finely chopped

1 cup reduced-sodium **chicken broth**

3 tablespoons fresh **lemon juice**

2 teaspoons chopped **fresh basil**

Chicken Cacciatore

PREP	20 MINUTES
COOK	ABOUT 45 MINUTES
SERVES	6

1 Sprinkle the chicken with ½ teaspoon of the salt and ⅛ teaspoon of the pepper. Heat 2 teaspoons of the oil in a 12-inch nonstick skillet over medium-high heat. Add the chicken and cook until browned, about 3 minutes on each side. Transfer the chicken to a plate.

2 Heat the remaining 1 teaspoon oil in the same skillet over medium-high heat. Add the carrots, celery, onion, bell peppers, garlic, and marjoram; cook, stirring occasionally, until slightly softened, about 5 minutes. Stir in the tomatoes and their juice and the remaining ¼ teaspoon salt and ⅛ teaspoon pepper. Cook, stirring occasionally, until the sauce is bubbly and slightly thickened, about 4 minutes. Add the chicken, turning to coat with the sauce. Reduce the heat and simmer, covered, turning the chicken and stirring occasionally, until the chicken is cooked through, 20–25 minutes.

3 Transfer the chicken to a platter; cover and keep warm. Bring the sauce in the skillet to a boil over medium-high heat. Cook until slightly thickened, about 4 minutes. Pour the sauce over the chicken.

PER SERVING (1 piece chicken with ⅔ cup sauce and vegetables): 273 Cal, 10 g Fat, 3 g Sat Fat, 0 g Trans Fat, 90 mg Chol, 651 mg Sod, 13 g Carb, 3 g Fib, 32 g Prot, 87 mg Calc. **POINTS** value: **6.**

GOOD IDEA If you happen to have some fresh mushrooms on hand, slice and add them to the vegetables in Step 2— their earthy flavor will add a subtle richness to the dish.

1 (3½-pound) **chicken**, cut into 6 pieces and skinned (wings discarded)

¾ teaspoon **salt**

¼ teaspoon freshly **ground pepper**

3 teaspoons **extra-virgin olive oil**

2 **carrots**, thinly sliced

2 **celery** stalks, chopped

1 **onion**, chopped

1 **red bell pepper**, seeded and chopped

1 **green bell pepper**, seeded and chopped

3 **garlic cloves**, minced

1½ teaspoons **dried marjoram**

1 (28-ounce) can Italian **plum tomatoes**, chopped

Chicken Cacciatore

Buffalo Chicken Salad with Buttermilk-Blue Cheese Dressing

PREP	**10 MINUTES**
COOK	**ABOUT 5 MINUTES**
SERVES	**4**

1 Drizzle the chicken with 2 tablespoons of the hot sauce, the barbecue sauce, and 1 of the minced garlic cloves in a medium bowl; toss to coat. Spray a nonstick ridged grill pan with nonstick spray and set over medium-high heat. Add the chicken and cook, until browned and cooked through, about 2½ minutes on each side.

2 Meanwhile, whisk the buttermilk, mayonnaise, vinegar, salt, pepper, and the remaining ½ teaspoon hot sauce and 1 minced garlic clove in a small bowl until smooth. Stir in the blue cheese and 2 tablespoons of the chives.

3 Arrange the romaine, carrots, celery, and tomatoes on a large platter. Top with the grilled chicken tenders; sprinkle the chicken with the remaining 1 tablespoon chives. Serve with the dressing.

PER SERVING (¼ of platter and 3 tablespoons dressing): 226 Cal, 8 g Fat, 4 g Sat Fat, 0 g Trans Fat, 66 mg Chol, 646 mg Sod, 12 g Carb, 3 g Fib, 25 g Prot, 183 mg Calc. **POINTS** value: **5.**

EXPRESS LANE If you want to make this quicker (and for the same **POINTS** value), instead of making a dressing, stir the blue cheese into ⅔ cup bottled fat-free Ranch dressing.

¾ pound **chicken tenders**

2 tablespoons + ½ teaspoon **Louisiana-style hot sauce**

1 tablespoon **barbecue sauce**

2 **garlic cloves**, minced

½ cup **fat-free buttermilk**

2 tablespoons **fat-free mayonnaise**

1 teaspoon **cider vinegar**

¼ teaspoon **salt**

¼ teaspoon freshly **ground pepper**

½ cup crumbled **blue cheese**

3 tablespoons minced **fresh chives**

1 (9-ounce) bag **hearts of romaine** salad

1 cup **baby carrots**

2 **celery** stalks, sliced

½ pint **cherry tomatoes**

Italian Grilled Chicken on White Bean Salad

PREP	10 MINUTES PLUS 3 MINUTES STANDING TIME
COOK	ABOUT 10 MINUTES
SERVES	4

1 Combine 3 tablespoons of the dressing, the beans, tomatoes, onion, parsley, and olives in a medium bowl.

2 Brush the chicken with the remaining 2 tablespoons dressing. Spray a nonstick, ridged grill pan with nonstick spray and set over medium-high heat. Add the chicken and cook, until browned and cooked through, 4–5 minutes on each side. Transfer the chicken to a cutting board, let stand about 3 minutes, then slice on the diagonal.

3 Meanwhile, divide the greens among 4 plates, then spoon about ½ cup of the bean salad on each plate. Top each with a sliced chicken breast.

PER SERVING (1 salad): 300 Cal, 6 g Fat, 2 g Sat Fat, 0 g Trans Fat, 86 mg Chol, 537 mg Sod, 22 g Carb, 6 g Fib, 39 g Prot, 74 mg Calc.
POINTS value: **6.**

HOW WE DID IT Allowing the chicken to rest for a few minutes before slicing will keep it tender and juicy. If you slice it immediately after taking it off the grill pan, the juices will run out, making the chicken dry.

5 tablespoons fat-free bottled Italian dressing

1 (15-ounce) can cannellini (white kidney) beans, rinsed and drained

½ cup halved grape tomatoes

¼ cup chopped red onion

¼ cup chopped fresh parsley

8 pitted kalamata olives, roughly chopped

4 (5-ounce) skinless boneless chicken breast halves

1 (5-ounce) bag prepared baby salad greens

Chicken with Sun-Dried Tomatoes and Swiss Cheese

PREP	5 MINUTES PLUS 10 MINUTES STANDING TIME
COOK	ABOUT 10 MINUTES
SERVES	4

2 cups **hot water**

6 **sun-dried tomatoes**
(not oil-packed)

4 (¼-pound) skinless
boneless **chicken
breast** halves

½ teaspoon **salt**

¼ teaspoon freshly
ground pepper

1 tablespoon **extra-virgin
olive oil**

4 (¾-ounce) slices **fat-
free Swiss cheese**

1 cup reduced-sodium
chicken broth

1 tablespoon **balsamic
vinegar**

1 teaspoon **dried
oregano**

1 Pour the hot water over the tomatoes in a small bowl. Let stand until the tomatoes are softened, about 10 minutes. Drain, then chop the tomatoes.

2 Meanwhile, sprinkle the chicken with ¼ teaspoon of the salt and ⅛ teaspoon of the pepper. Heat the oil in a medium nonstick skillet over medium-high heat. Add the chicken and cook until well browned, about 3 minutes. Turn the chicken and top each breast half with one-fourth of the tomatoes and 1 slice of the cheese. Cook about 1 minute. Add the broth, vinegar, oregano, and the remaining ¼ teaspoon salt and ⅛ teaspoon pepper. Bring the broth mixture to a boil and cook until the chicken is cooked though, about 3 minutes. Transfer the chicken to a plate with a slotted spoon; cover and keep warm.

3 Cook the broth mixture about 1 minute; pour the sauce over the chicken.

PER SERVING (1 chicken breast half with 2 tablespoons sauce): 198 Cal, 6 g Fat, 1 g Sat Fat, 0 g Trans Fat, 63 mg Chol, 844 mg Sod, 5 g Carb, 1 g Fib, 29 g Prot, 122 mg Calc. **POINTS** value: **4.**

GOOD IDEA Serve this dish with steamed red potatoes (1 cup cooked potatoes for each serving will increase the **POINTS** value by 2). You can also top the chicken with slices of fat-free mozzarella cheese instead of the Swiss.

Chicken Hobo Packets

PREP	15 MINUTES
COOK	ABOUT 20 MINUTES
SERVES	4

1 Preheat the oven to 425°F. Sprinkle the chicken with ¼ teaspoon of the salt and ⅛ teaspoon of the pepper. Heat 2 teaspoons of the oil in a medium nonstick skillet over medium-high heat until the oil just begins to smoke. Add the chicken and cook until lightly browned, about 1 minute on each side. Transfer the chicken to a plate.

2 Heat the remaining 2 teaspoons oil in the same skillet over medium-high heat. Add the zucchini, bell pepper, and the remaining ½ teaspoon salt and ⅛ teaspoon pepper; cook, stirring occasionally, until slightly softened, about 3 minutes.

3 Tear off 4 (18-inch) sheets of foil. Place a chicken breast in the center of each sheet; top each with ½ cup vegetable mixture and ¼ cup salsa. Fold each piece of foil into a packet, making a tight seal and allowing room for the packets to expand.

4 Transfer the packets to a baking sheet. Bake until the chicken is cooked through, 12–15 minutes. Open the packets carefully when testing for doneness, as steam will escape. Serve, sprinkled with the cilantro.

PER SERVING (1 packet): 197 Cal, 7 g Fat, 1 g Sat Fat, 0 g Trans Fat, 63 mg Chol, 933 mg Sod, 7 g Carb, 1 g Fib, 24 g Prot, 22 mg Calc. **POINTS** value: **4.**

EXPRESS LANE Get a jumpstart on dinner tonight by prepping the recipe ahead through Step 3. The packets can be refrigerated up to 4 hours. When ready to bake, allow the packets to stand at room temperature for 15 minutes while the oven preheats.

4 (¼-pound) skinless boneless **chicken breast** halves

¾ teaspoon **salt**

⅛ teaspoon freshly **ground pepper**

4 teaspoons **extra-virgin olive oil**

1 **zucchini**, halved lengthwise and cut into ⅛-inch-thick slices

1 **red bell pepper**, seeded cut into thin slices

1 cup **fat-free mild chunky salsa**

2 tablespoons chopped **fresh cilantro**

Chicken Negimaki

Chicken Negimaki

PREP	15 MINUTES PLUS 2 HOURS CHILLING TIME
COOK	10-12 MINUTES
SERVES	4

1 Place a chicken breast between 2 sheets of plastic wrap. Pound the chicken to ¼-inch thickness, using a meat mallet or bottom of heavy saucepan. Repeat with remaining chicken. Arrange the chicken on a work surface with long side facing you, then top each with 1 of the scallions, lengthwise. Roll the chicken around the scallions, jelly-roll style, and secure with kitchen string at 1-inch intervals.

2 Combine the soy sauce, vinegar, ginger, and garlic in a shallow bowl. Add the chicken rolls and toss well to coat. Cover and refrigerate, turning occasionally, at least 2 hours or overnight.

3 Remove the chicken rolls from the marinade; discard the marinade. Heat the oil in a medium nonstick skillet over medium heat. Add the chicken rolls and cook, turning often, until browned and cooked through, 10–12 minutes. Transfer the rolls to a cutting board and remove the string. Cut each roll into 6 pieces.

PER SERVING (6 pieces negimaki): 146 Cal, 5 g Fat, 1 g Sat Fat, 0 g Trans Fat, 63 mg Chol, 131 mg Sod, 1 g Carb, 0 g Fib, 23 g Prot, 16 mg Calc. *POINTS* value: **3.**

GOOD IDEA If you want a grilled look, cook the chicken in a ridged grill pan instead of a skillet.

4 (¼-pound) skinless boneless **chicken breast** halves

4 **scallions**, dark green part only

2 tablespoons reduced-sodium **soy sauce**

1 tablespoon **rice vinegar**

1 tablespoon minced peeled **fresh ginger**

1 **garlic clove**, minced

2 teaspoons **canola oil**

Chicken Curry Sauté

PREP	10 MINUTES
COOK	ABOUT 10 MINUTES
SERVES	4

1 Heat 2 teaspoons of the oil in a large nonstick skillet over medium-high heat. Add the chicken and cook, stirring frequently, until browned and cooked through, about 3 minutes. Transfer the chicken to a plate.

2 Heat the remaining 2 teaspoons oil in the same skillet over medium-high heat. Add the onion, garlic, and ginger; cook, stirring occasionally, until slightly softened, about 2 minutes. Add the carrots and curry powder; cook, stirring frequently, until fragrant, about 1 minute. Stir in the broth and tomato paste; bring to a boil. Boil until the liquid starts to thicken and the vegetables are crisp-tender, about 2 minutes. Stir in the chicken, tomatoes, and salt; cook, stirring occasionally, until heated through, about 1 minute.

PER SERVING (¾ cup): 217 Cal, 7 g Fat, 1 g Sat Fat, 0 g Trans Fat, 63 mg Chol, 341 mg Sod, 12 g Carb, 3 g Fib, 25 g Prot, 36 mg Calc. **POINTS** value: **4.**

- 4 teaspoons **extra-virgin olive oil**
- 1 pound skinless boneless **chicken breasts**, cut into 1½ x ¼-inch strips
- 1 **onion**, chopped
- 2 **garlic cloves**, minced
- 2 teaspoons minced peeled **fresh ginger**
- 2 **carrots**, sliced ¼-inch thick
- 1½ teaspoons **curry powder**
- ¾ cup reduced-sodium **chicken broth**
- 1 tablespoon **tomato paste**
- 1 cup **grape tomatoes**, halved
- ¼ teaspoon **salt**

Cajun Chicken with Creamy Corn, Okra, and Tomato

PREP	10 MINUTES
COOK	ABOUT 10 MINUTES
SERVES	4

1 Mix the flour and ½ teaspoon of the Cajun seasoning in a zip-close plastic bag. Add the chicken; seal the bag and shake to coat the chicken.

2 Heat 1½ teaspoons of the oil in a large nonstick skillet over medium-high heat. Add the chicken strips and cook, turning occasionally, until lightly browned and cooked through, about 4 minutes. Transfer the chicken to a plate.

3 Add the remaining ½ teaspoon oil to the same skillet, then add the onion. Cook over medium-high heat, stirring often, until browned, about 3 minutes. Add the corn and okra; cook, stirring occasionally, until almost tender, about 2 minutes. Add the half-and-half, the remaining ¾ teaspoon Cajun seasoning and the salt; bring to a simmer. Simmer until slightly thickened, about 1 minute. Add the tomato and return the chicken to the skillet; heat through, about 2 minutes.

PER SERVING (1 cup): 216 Cal, 5 g Fat, 1 g Sat Fat, 0 g Trans Fat, 54 mg Chol, 407 mg Sod, 20 g Carb, 3 g Fib, 22 g Prot, 98 mg Calc. **POINTS** value: **4.**

EXPRESS LANE To quickly thaw frozen okra and corn, place them in a colander and run cold water over them. Drain well before using.

2 tablespoons all-purpose flour

1¼ teaspoons Cajun seasoning

¾ pound skinless boneless chicken breasts, cut into about 20 strips

2 teaspoons canola oil

1 small onion, chopped

1 cup frozen corn kernels, thawed

1 cup frozen cut okra, thawed

½ cup fat-free half-and-half

¼ teaspoon salt

1 large plum tomato, chopped

Cranberry-Pear Chicken

PREP	10 MINUTES
COOK	ABOUT 12 MINUTES
SERVES	4

1 Combine the flour, ¼ teaspoon of the salt, and ¼ teaspoon of the pepper on a sheet of wax paper. Add the chicken and toss to coat.

2 Heat 1½ teaspoons of the oil in a large nonstick skillet over medium-high heat. Add the chicken and cook, turning occasionally, until browned and cooked through, about 5 minutes. Transfer the chicken to a plate.

3 Add the remaining ½ teaspoon oil to the same skillet, then add the pear and scallions. Cook over medium-high heat, stirring often, until the pear is golden, about 3 minutes. Add the pear nectar, cranberries, and the remaining ¼ teaspoon salt and ¼ teaspoon pepper. Increase the heat to high and cook, stirring occaisionally, until the sauce bubbles and thickens slightly, about 3 minutes. Stir in the mustard; return the chicken to the skillet and heat through, about 1 minute.

PER SERVING (1 cup): 217 Cal, 5 g Fat, 1 g Sat Fat, 0 g Trans Fat, 51 mg Chol, 373 mg Sod, 23 g Carb, 3 g Fib, 20 g Prot, 28 mg Calc. **POINTS** value: *4.*

GOOD IDEA If you like, you can substitute apple cider for the pear nectar and serve with steamed asparagus.

1½ tablespoons **all-purpose flour**

½ teaspoon **salt**

½ teaspoon freshly **ground pepper**

¾ pound skinless boneless **chicken breasts**, cut into 1-inch pieces

2 teaspoons **canola oil**

1 ripe **pear**, peeled, cored, and chopped

3 **scallions**, sliced

¾ cup **pear nectar**

¼ cup **dried cranberries**

2 teaspoons **coarse-grain mustard**

Cranberry-Pear Chicken

Microwave Moroccan Chicken Stew

PREP	15 MINUTES
COOK	ABOUT 15 MINUTES
SERVES	6

1 Combine the chicken, jalapeño, 2 teaspoons of the oil, the coriander, cumin, and cinnamon in a medium bowl. Cover and refrigerate while preparing the vegetables.

2 Combine the carrots, onion, garlic, and the remaining 1 teaspoon oil in a 3-quart microwavable casserole with a lid. Cover and microwave on High until the onions soften, $3\frac{1}{2}$–4 minutes. Stir in the tomatoes, broth, and zucchini; microwave on High, covered, stirring once halfway through cooking, $3\frac{1}{2}$–4 minutes. Stir in the chicken mixture and microwave on High, covered, until almost cooked through, $2\frac{1}{2}$–3 minutes. Break up the chicken with a spoon. Stir in the chickpeas and salt; microwave on High, covered, until hot and the chicken is cooked through, $1\frac{1}{2}$–2 minutes.

PER SERVING ($1\frac{1}{3}$ cups): 199 Cal, 5 g Fat, 1 g Sat Fat, 0 g Trans Fat, 42 mg Chol, 577 mg Sod, 19 g Carb, 6 g Fib, 20 g Prot, 64 mg Calc. **POINTS** value: **4.**

GOOD IDEA Serve this dish with a side of whole-wheat couscous ($\frac{2}{3}$ cup cooked couscous for each serving would increase the **POINTS** value by 2).

1 pound skinless boneless **chicken breasts**, cut into 1-inch chunks

1 **jalapeño pepper**, seeded and minced (wear gloves to prevent irritation)

3 teaspoons **olive oil**

$\frac{1}{4}$ teaspoon **ground coriander**

$\frac{1}{4}$ teaspoon **ground cumin**

$\frac{1}{4}$ teaspoon **cinnamon**

4 **carrots**, sliced $\frac{1}{4}$-inch thick

1 **onion**, chopped

1 **garlic clove**, minced

1 ($14\frac{1}{2}$-ounce) can diced **tomatoes**, drained

1 cup reduced-sodium **chicken broth**

2 medium **zucchini**, diced

$\frac{3}{4}$ cup canned **chickpeas**, rinsed and drained

$\frac{1}{2}$ teaspoon **salt**

Caribbean Black Beans and Chicken

PREP	10 MINUTES
COOK	ABOUT 12 MINUTES
SERVES	4

1 Heat 1 teaspoon of the oil in a large nonstick skillet over medium-high heat. Add the chicken; sprinkle with ¼ teaspoon of the salt and cook, turning occasionally, until browned and cooked through, about 5 minutes. Transfer to a plate.

2 Add the remaining ½ teaspoon oil to the same skillet, then add the onion, jalapeños, ginger, and garlic. Cook over medium-high heat, stirring often, until the onion is golden, about 4 minutes.

3 Stir in the black beans, orange juice, thyme, allspice, and the remaining ¼ teaspoon salt; bring to a boil. Reduce the heat and simmer, uncovered, until the flavors blend, about 2 minutes. Return the chicken to the skillet and heat through, about 1 minute. Serve with the pineapple and cilantro.

PER SERVING (1 cup chicken mixture and ¼ cup pineapple): 274 Cal, 5 g Fat, 1 g Sat Fat, 0 g Trans Fat, 51 mg Chol, 623 mg Sod, 31 g Carb, 6 g Fib, 26 g Prot, 78 mg Calc. *POINTS* value: **5.**

PLAY IT SAFE We suggest using gloves when handling jalapeños. Although they vary in heat level, they can be quite hot, so it's best to use caution.

1½ teaspoons canola oil

¾ pound skinless boneless chicken breasts, cut into 1-inch pieces

½ teaspoon salt

1 small onion, chopped

2 large jalapeño peppers, seeded and minced (wear gloves to prevent irritation)

1 tablespoon minced peeled fresh ginger

2 garlic cloves, minced

1 (15-ounce) can black beans, rinsed and drained

½ cup orange juice

½ teaspoon dried thyme

¼ teaspoon ground allspice

1 cup diced fresh pineapple

¼ cup chopped fresh cilantro

Chicken Fajita Skillet

PREP	20 MINUTES
COOK	ABOUT 15 MINUTES
SERVES	4

1 Combine the tomatoes, avocado, cilantro, and lime juice in a medium bowl.

2 Heat 1 teaspoon of the oil in a large nonstick skillet over medium-high heat. Add half the chicken and cook, stirring occasionally, until browned and cooked through, about 4 minutes. Transfer the chicken to a plate. Repeat with the remaining chicken.

3 Heat the remaining 1 teaspoon oil in the same skillet over medium-high heat. Add the onion and bell peppers; cook, stirring occasionally, until the vegetables are very soft, about 5 minutes. Add the chicken and Mexican seasoning; cook, stirring frequently, about 1 minute. Stir in the soy sauce and cook until liquid almost evaporates, about 30 seconds. Serve with the salsa.

PER SERVING (1 cup chicken mixture with ½ cup salsa): 227 Cal, 8 g Fat, 2 g Sat Fat, 0 g Trans Fat, 63 mg Chol, 446 mg Sod, 13 g Carb, 4 g Fib, 26 g Prot, 27 mg Calc. **POINTS** value: **4.**

GOOD IDEA If you don't have Mexican seasoning handy on your spice shelf, substitute an equal amount of taco seasoning. You might like to accompany each serving with a tortilla and deduct it from your **weekly POINTS** Allowance (a 7-inch whole-wheat tortilla will increase the **POINTS** value by 1).

1 pint **cherry tomatoes**, quartered

½ medium **avocado**, peeled and cut into ¼-inch cubes

2 tablespoons chopped **fresh cilantro**

1 tablespoon fresh **lime juice**

2 teaspoons **olive oil**

1 pound skinless boneless **chicken breasts**, cut into 1½ x ¼-inch strips

1 **onion**, sliced

1 **red bell pepper**, seeded and cut into ¼-inch-thick strips

1 **green bell pepper**, seeded and cut into ¼-inch-inch strips

1 teaspoon **Mexican seasoning**

2 tablespoons reduced-sodium **soy sauce**

Quick Chicken Mole

PREP	10 MINUTES
COOK	ABOUT 10 MINUTES
SERVES	4

1 Heat a large nonstick skillet over medium-high heat. Add the pumpkin seeds and cook, stirring frequently, until toasted, about 1 minute. Transfer the seeds to a plate to cool.

2 Sprinkle the chicken with 1 teaspoon of the chili powder and the salt. Heat the oil in the same skillet over medium-high heat. Add the chicken and cook until browned and cooked through, about 2 minutes on each side. Transfer the chicken to a serving plate; cover and keep warm.

3 Add the tomatoes, cocoa, cumin, cinnamon, and the remaining ½ teaspoon chili powder to the skillet; bring to a boil, scraping any browned bits from the bottom of the pan. Reduce the heat and simmer until slightly thickened, about 2 minutes. Stir in the peanut butter, then spoon the sauce over the chicken. Sprinkle with the toasted pumpkin seeds and the cilantro.

PER SERVING (1 piece chicken, ¼ cup sauce, and 1 tablespoon pumpkin seeds): 221 Cal, 11 g Fat, 2 g Sat Fat, 0 g Trans Fat, 51 mg Chol, 365 mg Sod, 8 g Carb, 2 g Fib, 25 g Prot, 54 mg Calc.
POINTS value: **5.**

¼ cup shelled **pumpkin seeds**

4 (3-ounce) thin-sliced **chicken breast cutlets**

1½ teaspoons **chili powder**

¼ teaspoon **salt**

1 teaspoon **canola oil**

1 (14½-ounce) can fire-roasted diced **tomatoes**

1 teaspoon unsweetened **cocoa powder**

½ teaspoon **ground cumin**

⅛ teaspoon **cinnamon**

1 teaspoon **peanut butter**

¼ cup chopped **cilantro**

Tuscan-Style Chicken Thighs

Tuscan-Style Chicken Thighs

PREP	15 MINUTES PLUS 2 HOURS CHILLING TIME
COOK	30-35 MINUTES
SERVES	6

1 Combine the garlic, shallot, rosemary, oil, mustard, lemon juice, and lemon zest in a zip-close plastic bag; add the chicken. Squeeze out the air and seal the bag; turn to coat the chicken. Refrigerate, turning the bag occasionally, at least 2 hours or overnight.

2 Preheat the oven to 450°F. Place the rack of a roasting pan in the pan; spray with canola nonstick spray. Remove the chicken from the marinade; discard the marinade. Transfer the chicken to the pan and sprinkle with the salt and pepper. Roast the chicken until cooked through, 30–35 minutes.

PER SERVING (1 chicken thigh): 157 Cal, 8 g Fat, 2 g Sat Fat, 0 g Trans Fat, 69 mg Chol, 461 mg Sod, 1 g Carb, 0 g Fib, 19 g Prot, 11 mg Calc. *POINTS* value: *4.*

PLAY IT SAFE A good way to test for doneness is to insert an instant-read thermometer into the thickest part of each thigh without touching the bone. The temperature should register 180°F.

3 **garlic cloves**, minced

1 small **shallot**, chopped

1 tablespoon chopped **fresh rosemary**

1 tablespoon **extra-virgin olive oil**

1 tablespoon **Dijon mustard**

1 tablespoon fresh **lemon juice**

1 teaspoon grated **lemon zest**

6 bone-in **chicken thighs**, skinned, about 2¼ pounds

1 teaspoon **salt**

¼ teaspoon freshly **ground pepper**

Middle Eastern Chicken Thighs with Peppers and Onions

PREP	10 MINUTES
COOK	ABOUT 12 MINUTES
SERVES	4

1 Preheat the broiler. Line a broiler rack with foil, then spray the foil with nonstick spray.

2 Combine the broth, oil, lemon zest, lemon juice, garlic, paprika, cumin, and salt in a large bowl. Remove and reserve ¼ cup. Add the chicken, bell peppers, and onion to the large bowl and toss to coat. Place the chicken, bell peppers, and onion on the broiler rack.

3 Broil, 4 inches from the heat, turning the chicken and vegetables once, until the chicken is cooked through and the vegetables are tender, about 12 minutes. Transfer to a serving platter, drizzle with the reserved ¼ cup broth mixture, and sprinkle with the parsley.

PER SERVING (2 pieces chicken and generous ½ cup vegetables): 277 Cal, 14 g Fat, 4 g Sat Fat, 0 g Trans Fat, 88 mg Chol, 450 mg Sod, 6 g Carb, 2 g Fib, 31 g Prot, 57 mg Calc. **POINTS** value: **6.**

GOOD IDEA Instead of coating the foil with nonstick spray, look for an even easier cut-the-cleanup option—nonstick foil, a new product available in most supermarkets.

½ cup reduced-sodium **chicken broth**

2 teaspoons **extra-virgin olive oil**

1½ teaspoons grated **lemon zest**

3 tablespoons **lemon juice**

2 **garlic cloves**, minced

1 teaspoon **paprika**

1 teaspoon **ground cumin**

½ teaspoon **salt**

4 (5-ounce) skinless boneless **chicken thighs**, cut in half

2 small **red bell peppers**, seeded and quartered

½ cup sliced **onion**

¼ cup chopped **fresh parsley**

Greek Tomato-Feta Chicken Cutlets

PREP	5 MINUTES
COOK	ABOUT 10 MINUTES
SERVES	4

1 Sprinkle the chicken with the oregano and ¼ teaspoon each of the salt and pepper. Heat 1 teaspoon of the oil in a large nonstick skillet over medium-high heat. Add the chicken and cook until browned and cooked through, about 2 minutes on each side. Transfer the chicken to a serving plate; cover and keep warm.

2 Add the remaining ½ teaspoon oil to the same skillet, then add the tomatoes, garlic, lemon zest, and the remaining ¼ teaspoon each salt and pepper. Cook over medium-high heat, stirring often, until the tomatoes soften and collapse, about 3 minutes.

3 Spoon the sauce over the chicken then sprinkle with the cucumber, cheese, and mint.

PER SERVING (1 piece chicken, ¼ cup sauce, 2 tablespoons cucumber, and 1 tablespoon each feta cheese and mint): 163 Cal, 6 g Fat, 2 g Sat Fat, 0 g Trans Fat, 55 mg Chol, 481 mg Sod, 6 g Carb, 2 g Fib, 21 g Prot, 74 mg Calc. **POINTS** value: **3.**

GOOD IDEA Warm pita bread would be nice on the side of this dish—1 small (1-ounce) pita would increase the **POINTS** value by 1.

4 (3-ounce) thin-sliced **chicken breast** cutlets

1 teaspoon dried **oregano**

½ teaspoon **salt**

½ teaspoon freshly **ground pepper**

1½ teaspoons **olive oil**

1 pint **cherry tomatoes**

1 **garlic clove**, minced

½ teaspoon grated **lemon zest**

½ cup diced **cucumber**

¼ cup crumbled **reduced-fat feta cheese**

¼ cup chopped **fresh mint**

Beijing Chicken Wraps

PREP	10 MINUTES
COOK	ABOUT 5 MINUTES
SERVES	4

1 Spread the cornstarch on a sheet of wax paper. Add the chicken and toss until coated. Heat the oil in a large nonstick skillet over medium-high heat. Add the chicken and cook until browned and cooked through, about 2 minutes on each side. Transfer the chicken to a plate.

2 Add the scallions to the same skillet and stir-fry until crisp-tender, about 2 minutes. Return the chicken to the skillet and add 1 tablespoon of the hoisin sauce; stir-fry over low heat until coated.

3 Line each tortilla with 1 lettuce leaf, 2 chicken tenders, 3 tablespoons scallions, 2 tablespoons radishes, and ½ tablespoon peanuts. Roll up and serve with the remaining ¼ cup hoisin sauce for dipping.

PER SERVING (1 wrap and 1 tablespoon hoisin sauce): 337 Cal, 9 g Fat, 1 g Sat Fat, 0 g Trans Fat, 51 mg Chol, 734 mg Sod, 39 g Carb, 3 g Fib, 25 g Prot, 94 mg Calc. **POINTS** value: **7.**

ZAP IT Warm the tortillas between damp paper towels in the microwave on High for 1 minute. They'll become very soft and pliable.

2 tablespoons **cornstarch**

8 **chicken tenders** (about ¾ pound)

2 teaspoons **canola oil**

8 **scallions**, cut into 2-inch pieces

1 tablespoon + ¼ cup **hoisin sauce**

4 (7–8-inch) fat-free **flour tortillas**, warmed

4 leaves **Boston lettuce**

½ cup diced **radishes**

2 tablespoons chopped **unsalted peanuts**

Chicken Souvlaki with Rice and Yogurt Sauce

PREP	**15 MINUTES PLUS 10 MINUTES STANDING TIME**
COOK	**ABOUT 5 MINUTES**
SERVES	**4**

1 Combine the chicken, vinegar, 1 of the minced garlic cloves, the oregano, and ¼ teaspoon each of the salt and pepper in a medium bowl; let stand 10 minutes.

2 Meanwhile, combine the yogurt, cucumber, mint, remaining minced garlic clove, and remaining ½ teaspoon each salt and pepper in a small bowl.

3 Heat the oil in a large nonstick skillet over medium-high heat. Add the chicken and cook until browned and cooked through, about 2 minutes on each side.

4 Arrange ½ cup rice on each of 4 plates; top with ½ cup shredded lettuce, 2 chicken tenders, one-fourth of tomato, one-fourth of onion, and ¼ cup of the yogurt sauce.

PER SERVING (1 plate): 282 Cal, 6 g Fat, 1 g Sat Fat, 0 g Trans Fat, 52 mg Chol, 658 mg Sod, 31 g Carb, 4 g Fib, 25 g Prot, 138 mg Calc. *POINTS* value: **5.**

EXPRESS LANE Save time and pick up cooked brown rice from your local Chinese take-out restaurant.

☑

8 **chicken tenders** (about ¾ pound)

2 tablespoons **red-wine vinegar**

2 **garlic cloves**, minced

1 teaspoon dried **oregano**

½ teaspoon **salt**

½ teaspoon freshly **ground pepper**

¾ cup plain **fat-free yogurt**

⅓ cup diced **cucumber**

¼ cup chopped **fresh mint**

2 teaspoons **olive oil**

2 cups hot cooked **brown rice**

2 cups shredded **lettuce**

1 **tomato**, chopped (about 1 cup)

½ cup thinly sliced **red onion**

Casablanca Chicken Kebabs

PREP	15 MINUTES PLUS 2 HOURS CHILLING AND 30 MINUTES STANDING TIME
COOK	ABOUT 15 MINUTES
SERVES	4

1 Combine the oil, lemon juice, lemon zest, orange zest, cumin, coriander, saffron, cinnamon, and pepper in a zip-close plastic bag; add the chicken. Squeeze out the air and seal the bag; turn to coat the chicken. Refrigerate, turning the bag occasionally, at least 2 hours or up to 4 hours.

2 Spray the grill rack with nonstick spray; prepare the grill. If using wooden skewers, soak them in water for 30 minutes.

3 Alternately thread the chicken and zucchini onto 4 (10-inch) metal or wooden skewers. Sprinkle the kebabs with the salt and place on the grill rack. Grill the kebabs, turning every 2 minutes, until the chicken is cooked through, about 15 minutes. Serve with lemon wedges.

PER SERVING (1 kebab): 138 Cal, 7 g Fat, 2 g Sat Fat, 0 g Trans Fat, 56 mg Chol, 635 mg Sod, 2 g Carb, 1 g Fib, 16 g Prot, 17 mg Calc. **POINTS** value: **3.**

1 tablespoon **extra-virgin olive oil**

1 tablespoon fresh **lemon juice**

2 teaspoons grated **lemon zest**

1 teaspoon grated **orange zest**

1 teaspoon **ground cumin**

½ teaspoon **ground coriander**

¼ teaspoon **ground saffron**

⅛ teaspoon **cinnamon**

¼ teaspoon freshly **ground pepper**

¾ pound skinless boneless **chicken thighs**, cut into 1-inch pieces

1 **zucchini**, halved lengthwise and cut crosswise into 16 pieces

1 teaspoon **salt**

Lemon wedges

Casablanca Chicken Kebabs

Chicken Paprikash

PREP	10 MINUTES
COOK	ABOUT 15 MINUTES
SERVES	4

1 Sprinkle the chicken with the salt. Heat 1 teaspoon of the oil in a large nonstick skillet over medium-high heat. Add the chicken and cook, turning occasionally, until browned and cooked through, about 6 minutes. Transfer to a plate.

2 Add the remaining ½ teaspoon oil to the same skillet, then add the onion and bell pepper. Cook over medium-high heat, stirring often, until softened, about 5 minutes. Add the paprika and flour; cook, stirring constantly, about 1 minute. Stir in the tomatoes, broth, garlic, and caraway seeds; cook, stirring constantly, until the mixture bubbles and thickens slightly, about 2 minutes.

3 Return the chicken to the skillet, spoon the sauce over the chicken, and heat through, about 1 minute. Remove from the heat, then stir in the sour cream and dill.

PER SERVING (1¼ cups): 288 Cal, 12 g Fat, 4 g Sat Fat, 0 g Trans Fat, 74 mg Chol, 663 mg Sod, 17 g Carb, 4 g Fib, 28 g Prot, 101 mg Calc. **POINTS** value: **6.**

GOOD IDEA A creamy paprikash begs to be served over egg noodles (½ cup cooked egg noodles per serving will increase the **POINTS** value by 2). Pick up a package of fresh noodles, which cook faster than the dried, or, if time is really of the essence, serve with crusty bread to sop up the deliciously rich sauce (a 1-ounce chunk of bread will also increase the **POINTS** value by 2).

1 pound skinless boneless **chicken thighs**, cut into 2-inch chunks

½ teaspoon **salt**

1½ teaspoons **canola oil**

1 large **onion**, chopped

1 **green bell pepper**, seeded and thinly sliced

2 tablespoons **paprika**, preferably Hungarian

2 tablespoons **all-purpose flour**

1 (14½-ounce) can diced **tomatoes**

1 cup reduced-sodium **chicken broth**

2 **garlic cloves**, minced

1 teaspoon **caraway seeds**

3 tablespoons **light sour cream**

3 tablespoons chopped **fresh dill**

Sesame-Orange Chicken Stir-Fry

PREP	10 MINUTES
COOK	ABOUT 10 MINUTES
SERVES	4

1 Spread the sesame seeds on a sheet of wax paper. Coat the chicken in the seeds.

2 Heat 1 teaspoon of the oil in a large nonstick skillet or wok over medium-high heat until a drop of water sizzles. Add the chicken and stir-fry just until cooked through, about 6 minutes. Transfer the chicken to a plate.

3 Heat the remaining 1 teaspoon oil in the same skillet over high heat. Add the bok choy, bell pepper, and sugar snap peas; stir-fry until the vegetables are crisp-tender, 4–5 minutes. Add the stir-fry sauce, orange juice, and the chicken; cook, stirring constantly, until heated through, about 1 minute. Sprinkle with the scallions.

PER SERVING (1½ cups): 297 Cal, 14 g Fat, 4 g Sat Fat, 0 g Trans Fat, 71 mg Chol, 711 mg Sod, 13 g Carb, 4 g Fib, 29 g Prot, 156 mg Calc. **POINTS** value: **6.**

GOOD IDEA Not a real fan of spicy foods? Opt for regular stir-fry sauce instead of Szechuan sauce. Serve over quick-cooking white or brown rice (½ cup cooked rice will up the **POINTS** value by 2).

2 tablespoons **sesame seeds**

1 pound skinless boneless **chicken thighs**, cut into 1½-inch chunks

2 teaspoons **peanut** or **canola oil**

¾ pound **bok choy**, chopped (about 5 cups)

1 **red bell pepper**, seeded and thinly sliced

1 (8-ounce) bag fresh stringless **sugar snap peas**

⅓ cup bottled **Szechuan stir-fry sauce**

⅓ cup **orange juice**

¼ cup sliced **scallions**

Tandoori Chicken Thighs

PREP	10 MINUTES PLUS 8 HOURS CHILLING TIME
COOK	22–25 MINUTES
SERVES	4

1 Combine the yogurt, paprika, ginger, garlic, curry powder, cinnamon, and saffron in a zip-close plastic bag; add the chicken. Squeeze out the air and seal the bag; turn to coat the chicken. Refrigerate, turning the bag occasionally, at least 8 hours or overnight.

2 Preheat the oven to 450°F. Place the rack of a roasting pan in the pan; spray with canola nonstick spray. Remove the chicken from the marinade; discard the marinade. Transfer the chicken to the pan and sprinkle with the salt and pepper. Roast the chicken until cooked through, 22–25 minutes.

PER SERVING (1 chicken thigh): 169 Cal, 9 g Fat, 2 g Sat Fat, 0 g Trans Fat, 75 mg Chol, 364 mg Sod, 1 g Carb, 0 g Fib, 1 g Prot, 21 mg Calc. **POINTS** value: **4.**

GOOD IDEA We include saffron, which is fairly expensive in the fragrant spice mixture, or you can substitute an equal amount of turmeric, which is cheaper.

½ cup plain **fat-free yogurt**

1 tablespoon **paprika**

1 tablespoon minced peeled **fresh ginger**

1 **garlic clove**, minced

1 teaspoon **curry powder**

¼ teaspoon **cinnamon**

¼ teaspoon **saffron threads**

4 (¼-pound) skinless boneless **chicken thighs**

½ teaspoon **salt**

¼ teaspoon freshly **ground pepper**

Shortcut Chicken Picadillo

PREP	10 MINUTES
COOK	ABOUT 15 MINUTES
SERVES	4

1 cup quick-cooking **brown rice**

½ teaspoon **salt**

¾ pound ground skinless **chicken**

1 **onion**, chopped

1 small **red bell pepper**, seeded and chopped

2 **garlic cloves**, minced

1 teaspoon **ground cumin**

1 (16-ounce) jar fat-free mild chunky **salsa**

1 Prepare the rice with ¼ teaspoon of the salt according to package directions, omitting any fat.

2 Meanwhile, spray a large nonstick skillet with canola nonstick spray and set over medium-high heat. Add the chicken and cook, stirring frequently to break it up, until browned and cooked through, about 5 minutes.

3 Add the onion, bell pepper, garlic, and cumin; cook, stirring occasionally, until the vegetables are softened, about 4 minutes. Stir in the salsa and the remaining ¼ teaspoon salt; cook until heated through and slightly thickened, about 2 minutes. Serve the picadillo over the rice.

PER SERVING (1½ cups): 267 Cal, 3 g Fat, 1 g Sat Fat, 0 g Trans Fat, 47 mg Chol, 1,167 mg Sod, 37 g Carb, 3 g Fib, 20 g Prot, 40 mg Calc. **POINTS** value: **5.**

GOOD IDEA In Cuba, picadillo is served with black beans as well as with rice (add ½ cup cooked beans to each serving and increase the **POINTS** value by 2).

BLT Chicken and Corn Chowder

BLT Chicken and Corn Chowder

PREP	10 MINUTES
COOK	ABOUT 15 MINUTES
SERVES	4

1 Spray a large nonstick saucepan with nonstick spray and set over medium-high heat. Add the white parts of the scallions and the bacon. Cook, stirring occasionally, until the scallions are softened and the bacon is lightly browned, about 3 minutes. Meanwhile, whisk the milk and flour in a bowl until blended.

2 Stir the milk mixture, potato, corn, thyme, and salt into the saucepan; bring to a boil over high heat. Reduce the heat and simmer until the potatoes are tender, about 5 minutes.

3 Stir in the chicken, half of the remaining scallions, and ½ cup of the tomato; heat through, about 2 minutes. Serve the soup sprinkled with the lettuce and the remaining scallions and tomato.

PER SERVING (1½ cups): 305 Cal, 6 g Fat, 2 g Sat Fat, 0 g Trans Fat, 54 mg Chol, 634 mg Sod, 38 g Carb, 4 g Fib, 28 g Prot, 267 mg Calc. **POINTS** value: **6.**

FOOD NOTE If you have the time, fresh corn (which is now available year round) can be used instead of the frozen. You'll need about 4 ears to yield 2 cups of kernels.

6 **scallions**, sliced (keep white and green parts separate)

4 slices **turkey bacon**, diced

3 cups **fat-free milk**

2 tablespoons **all-purpose flour**

1 **Yukon Gold potato**, peeled and diced (about 1 cup)

2 cups frozen **corn kernels**

½ teaspoon **dried thyme**

½ teaspoon **salt**

1½ cups cubed cooked **chicken breast**

1 cup diced **tomato**

1 cup thinly shredded **romaine lettuce**

Tropical Chicken Salad

PREP	15 MINUTES
COOK	NONE
SERVES	4

1 Combine the mayonnaise, yogurt, mint, vinegar, and ginger in a large bowl; mix well. Add the chicken, pineapple, mango, orange, and onion; toss to coat.

2 Arrange 2 lettuce leaves on each of 4 plates. Top each plate with 1 cup of the chicken salad. Sprinkle with the chile pepper and serve at once.

PER SERVING (1 salad): 193 Cal, 3 g Fat, 1 g Sat Fat, 0 g Trans Fat, 46 mg Chol, 217 mg Sod, 24 g Carb, 3 g Fib, 18 g Prot, 76 mg Calc. *POINTS* value: *4.*

EXPRESS LANE Really in a hurry? Look for fresh-cut pineapple and mango chunks at your supermarket produce section.

⅓ cup **fat-free mayonnaise**

⅓ cup plain **fat-free yogurt**

¼ cup chopped **fresh mint**

1 tablespoon **rice-wine vinegar**

2 teaspoons minced peeled **fresh ginger**

1½ cups cubed cooked **chicken breast**

1½ cups fresh **pineapple** chunks

1 **mango**, peeled, seeded, and cut into ¾-inch chunks

½ small **orange**, chopped

⅓ cup chopped **red onion**

8 Boston **lettuce leaves**

1 **fresno** or **jalapeño pepper**, seeded and minced (wear gloves to prevent irritation)

Chicken Tostadas

PREP	10 MINUTES
COOK	ABOUT 10 MINUTES
SERVES	4

4 (6-inch) **corn tortillas**

1 cup canned spicy fat-free **refried beans**

¼ cup **chipotle salsa**

1 (10-ounce) package Southwestern-seasoned carved **roasted chicken breast**

½ cup shredded reduced-fat sharp **cheddar cheese**

1 cup shredded **lettuce**

1 large **tomato**, diced

¼ cup **fat-free sour cream**

¼ cup sliced **scallions**

1 Preheat the oven to 450°F. Place the tortillas in a single layer on a baking sheet and bake until lightly crisped, about 6 minutes.

2 Spread each tortilla with ¼ cup of the refried beans, then 1 tablespoon of the salsa, one-fourth of the chicken, then top each with 2 tablespoons of the cheese. Return to the oven and bake until heated through and the cheese begins to melt, about 3 minutes.

3 Top each with ¼ cup each of the lettuce and tomato, and 1 tablespoon each of the sour cream and scallions.

PER SERVING (1 tostada): 248 Cal, 4 g Fat, 1 g Sat Fat, 0 g Trans Fat, 48 mg Chol, 637 mg Sod, 28 g Carb, 5 g Fib, 25 g Prot, 204 mg Calc. **POINTS** value: **4.**

FOOD NOTE If you want to tone down the heat, used regular fat-free refried beans and a mild regular salsa.

Tex-Mex Turkey Meatloaf

PREP	10 MINUTES PLUS 10 MINUTES STANDING TIME
COOK	45–50 MINUTES
SERVES	6

1 Preheat the oven to 400°F. Spray a baking sheet with canola nonstick spray.

2 Combine the turkey, ½ cup of the salsa, the onion, corn, potato flakes, egg white, garlic, oregano, salt, and pepper in a large bowl. Transfer the mixture to the sheet and form into a 4 x 9-inch loaf. Spread the remaining ½ cup salsa over the top. Bake until an instant-read thermometer inserted into the center of the loaf registers 165°F, 45–50 minutes. Let stand about 10 minutes before slicing. Cut into 12 slices.

PER SERVING (2 slices meatloaf): 161 Cal, 1 g Fat, 0 g Sat Fat, 0 g Trans Fat, 74 mg Chol, 545 mg Sod, 8 g Carb, 1 g Fib, 28 g Prot, 15 mg Calc. **POINTS** value: **3.**

GOOD IDEA It's easy to kick up the heat a notch if you substitute hot salsa in place of the mild variety called for in the recipe.

1½ pounds ground skinless **turkey breast**

1 cup fat-free **mild chunky salsa**

1 small **onion**, finely chopped

½ cup frozen **corn kernels**

⅓ cup instant mashed **potato flakes**

1 **egg white**

2 **garlic cloves**, minced

1 teaspoon **dried oregano**

½ teaspoon **salt**

¼ teaspoon freshly **ground pepper**

Tarragon Turkey Burgers

PREP	10 MINUTES
COOK	ABOUT 15 MINUTES
SERVES	4

1 pound ground skinless **turkey breast**

½ **red onion**, chopped

1 large **egg**, lightly beaten

2 tablespoons chopped **fresh parsley**

1 **garlic clove**, minced

1½ teaspoons minced **fresh tarragon**, or ½ teaspoon dried

½ teaspoon **salt**

1 Spray the grill rack with nonstick spray; prepare the grill.

2 Combine the turkey, onion, egg, parsley, garlic, tarragon, and salt. Form into 4 (½-inch-thick) patties.

3 Place the patties on the grill rack and grill until an instant-read thermometer inserted in the side of a burger registers 165°F, 6–8 minutes on each side.

PER SERVING (1 burger): 169 Calories, 10 g Fat, 3 g Sat Fat, 0 g Trans Fat, 121 mg Chol, 390 mg Sod, 2 g Carb, 0 g Fib, 17 g Prot, 32 mg Calc. **POINTS** value: **4.**

HOW WE DID IT To keep these burgers from charring and to make sure they're cooked through, bank the hot coals around the edges of your grill. Sear each burger over the hot coals 2 minutes on each side. Then position them over the indirect heat in the center of the grill and finish cooking, 4 to 6 minutes on each side.

Spaghetti and Turkey
Meatballs

Spaghetti and Turkey Meatballs

PREP	20 MINUTES
COOK	ABOUT 35 MINUTES
SERVES	6

1 Preheat the oven to 400°F. Spray a baking sheet with olive oil nonstick spray.

2 Combine the turkey, half the garlic, the egg white, cornmeal, 1 teaspoon of the basil, the oregano, and ½ teaspoon of the salt in a bowl. With moistened hands, form into 18 balls. Place the meatballs about 1-inch apart on the sheet. Bake, turning once, until the meatballs are browned and cooked through, about 20 minutes. Set aside.

3 Meanwhile, the oil in a large saucepan over medium-high heat. Add the onion, the remaining garlic and 2 teaspoons basil; cook, stirring occasionally, until slightly softened, about 2 minutes. Stir in the tomatoes with their juice, the tomato paste, the remaining ½ teaspoon salt, and the pepper; bring to a boil. Reduce the heat and simmer, partially covered, until the sauce starts to thicken, 12–15 minutes. Stir in the meatballs and simmer until the sauce is thickened and the meatballs are heated through, about 10 minutes.

4 Meanwhile, cook the spaghetti according to package directions; drain in a colander. Divide the spaghetti among 6 shallow bowls; top each with the meatballs and sauce.

PER SERVING (1 cup pasta with 3 meatballs and about ½ cup sauce): 364 Cal, 4 g Fat, 1 g Sat Fat, 0 g Trans Fat, 50 mg Chol, 692 mg Sod, 55 g Carb, 9 g Fib, 30 g Prot, 103 mg Calc. **POINTS** value: **7**.

EXPRESS LANE Make a double batch of the meatballs and sauce and set aside half for another meal. Stored in an airtight container, they can be frozen up to 6 months.

☑

1 pound ground skinless **turkey breast**

4 **garlic cloves**, minced

1 **egg white**

1 tablespoon **cornmeal**

3 teaspoon **dried basil**

1 teaspoon **dried oregano**

1 teaspoon **salt**

1 tablespoon **extra-virgin olive oil**

1 **onion**, chopped

1 (28-ounce) can Italian **plum tomatoes**, chopped

1 (6-ounce) can **tomato paste**

¼ teaspoon freshly **ground pepper**

¾ pound **whole-wheat spaghetti**

CHAPTER 6

Fisherman's Catch

Cajun Blackened Salmon

PREP	5 MINUTES
COOK	ABOUT 10 MINUTES
SERVES	4

1 Combine the salt, paprika, cumin, coriander, thyme, and cayenne in a small bowl. Rub the spice mixture on the side of the salmon with no skin.

2 Heat the oil in a large nonstick skillet over medium-high heat. Add the salmon, skin-side up, and cook until fish is just opaque in the center, about 5 minutes on each side. Remove the skin before eating and serve with the lemon wedges.

PER SERVING (1 salmon fillet): 229 Cal, 8 g Fat, 1 g Sat Fat, 0 g Trans Fat, 97 mg Chol, 707 mg Sod, 1g Carb, 0 g Fib, 37 g Prot, 30 mg Calc. **POINTS** value: **5.**

GOOD IDEA If you don't have all the ingredients for the seasoning in this recipe, there are many Cajun spice mixes on the market—use about 1½ teaspoons and reduce the salt to ½ teaspoon.

1 teaspoon **salt**

¾ teaspoon **paprika**

½ teaspoon **ground cumin**

¼ teaspoon **ground coriander**

¼ teaspoon **dried thyme**

⅛ teaspoon **cayenne**

4 (6-ounce) **salmon fillets**

1 teaspoon **canola oil**

Lemon wedges

Salmon on a Bed of Kale

PREP	15 MINUTES PLUS 15 MINUTES STANDING TIME
COOK	ABOUT 20 MINUTES
SERVES	4

☑

2 **red bell peppers**

2 cups **water**

1 bunch **kale**, trimmed of tough stalks and torn into bite-size pieces

1 large **red onion**, thinly sliced

1 (1-inch) piece **fresh ginger**, peeled and cut into very thin strips

2 **garlic cloves**, thinly sliced

2 teaspoons **mustard seeds**

½ teaspoon **ground coriander**

½ teaspoon **ground cumin**

¼ teaspoon **salt**

¼ teaspoon freshly **ground pepper**

4 (¼-pound) **salmon** fillets, ½-inch thick, skinned

1 Preheat the broiler. Line a baking sheet with foil and place the bell peppers on it. Broil 5 inches from the heat, turning frequently with tongs, until the skins blister, about 15 minutes. Transfer the peppers to a counter and wrap in the foil. Let steam about 15 minutes. When cool enough to handle, peel them, discard the seeds, and cut into long strips.

2 Meanwhile, bring the water to a boil in a large deep nonstick skillet. Add the kale and cook, covered, until tender, 6–8 minutes. Drain in a colander.

3 Wipe out the skillet, spray with canola nonstick spray, and set over medium heat. Add the onion, ginger, and garlic; cook, stirring frequently, until the onion is light golden brown on the edges, about 5 minutes. Stir in the mustard seeds, coriander, cumin, and ⅛ teaspoon each of the salt and pepper; cook, stirring frequently, until fragrant, about 1 minute. Remove the skillet from the heat and set aside.

4 Spray the broiler rack with canola nonstick spray. Sprinkle the salmon with the remaining ⅛ teaspoon each salt and pepper. Broil the salmon 5 inches from the heat until just opaque in the center, 5–7 minutes.

5 Meanwhile, return the skillet to the heat. Add the kale and roasted pepper; cook, turning constantly with tongs, until well combined and heated through, about 4 minutes. Divide the kale mixture among 4 plates; top with the salmon.

PER SERVING (1 salmon fillet and ¾ cup kale mixture): 214 Cal, 5 g Fat, 1 g Sat Fat, 0 g Trans Fat, 65 mg Chol, 256 mg Sod, 14 g Carb, 4 g Fib, 28 g Prot, 120 mg Calc. **POINTS** value: **4.**

Barbecue Salmon
with Ginger

Barbecue Salmon with Ginger

PREP	5 MINUTES PLUS 5 MINUTES COOLING TIME
COOK	ABOUT 15 MINUTES
SERVES	4

1 Preheat the oven to 500°F. Spray a baking sheet with canola nonstick spray.

2 Meanwhile, combine the ketchup, lemon juice, soy sauce, and ginger in a small saucepan. Bring to a boil over medium heat. Reduce the heat and simmer, stirring occasionally, until thickened, about 4 minutes. Remove the saucepan from the heat; stir in the orange zest. Cool 5 minutes.

3 Place the salmon 2 inches apart on the sheet. Brush the salmon with the barbecue sauce. Roast until the fish is just opaque in the center, 10–12 minutes.

PER SERVING (1 salmon fillet): 244 Cal, 7 g Fat, 1 g Sat Fat, 0 g Trans Fat, 97 mg Chol, 662 mg Sod, 7 g Carb, 0 g Fib, 38 g Prot, 30 mg Calc. **POINTS** value: **5.**

GOOD IDEA You can serve this dish hot, at room temperature, or chilled with a side of steamed yellow summer squash and sugar sanp peas.

- ⅓ cup **ketchup**
- 2 tablespoons **fresh lemon juice**
- 2 teaspoons reduced-sodium **soy sauce**
- ⅛ teaspoon **ground ginger**
- 1 teaspoon grated **orange zest**
- 4 (6-ounce) **salmon fillets**, skinned

Herbed Salmon Burgers
with Tomato Salsa

PREP	10 MINUTES
COOK	ABOUT 10 MINUTES
SERVES	4

1 To make the salsa, combine the tomatoes, 1 tablespoon of the onion, the vinegar, oil, ¼ teaspoon of the salt, and ⅛ teaspoon of the pepper in a small bowl.

2 Put the salmon in a food processor; pulse until finely chopped. Transfer to a large bowl. Add the remaining onion, ½ teaspoon salt, and ⅛ teaspoon pepper, the basil, and oregano; mix well. Form the mixture into 4 patties, about ½-inch thick.

3 Spray a large nonstick skillet with olive oil nonstick spray and set over medium-high heat. Add the patties and cook, turning once, until well browned and cooked through, about 4 minutes on each side. Serve the burgers with the salsa.

PER SERVING (1 burger with 2 tablespoons salsa): 167 Cal, 6 g Fat, 1 g Sat Fat, 0 g Trans Fat, 65 mg Chol, 522 mg Sod, 3 g Carb, 1 g Fib, 25 g Prot, 30 mg Calc. **POINTS** value: **4.**

EXPRESS LANE Uncooked salmon patties can be frozen for up to 3 months, so double the recipe for another tasty meal to have at your fingertips. (Simply defrost the patties in the refrigerator overnight before cooking.) To cut down on the prep, use store-bought fat-free salsa and omit Step 1.

2 **plum tomatoes**, seeded and finely chopped

½ small **onion**, finely chopped

1 teaspoon **balsamic vinegar**

1 teaspoon **extra-virgin olive oil**

¾ teaspoon **salt**

¼ teaspoon freshly **ground pepper**

1 pound **salmon** fillet, skinned and cut into small chunks

¼ cup chopped **fresh basil**

4 teaspoons chopped **fresh oregano**

Arctic Char with Warm Fruited Couscous

PREP	10 MINUTES PLUS 5 MINUTES STANDING TIME
COOK	ABOUT 6 MINUTES
SERVES	4

¾ cup **water**

½ cup **orange juice**

1 teaspoon **ground coriander**

1 teaspoon **salt**

1 cup **couscous**

⅓ cup **golden raisins**

½ cup chopped **red onion**

⅓ cup chopped **fresh parsley**

2 tablespoons **raspberry vinegar**

1 teaspoon **olive oil**

4 (¼-pound) pieces **arctic char fillet**

1 Bring the water, orange juice, ½ teaspoon of the coriander, and ¾ teaspoon of the salt to a boil in a medium saucepan. Stir in the couscous and raisins, remove the saucepan from the heat, cover and let stand 5 minutes. Fluff the mixture with a fork. Stir in the onion, parsley, vinegar, and oil.

2 Sprinkle the arctic char with the remaining ½ teaspoon coriander and ¼ teaspoon salt. Spray a large nonstick skillet with nonstick spray and set over medium-high heat. Add the artic char and cook until just opaque in the center, about 3 minutes on each side. Serve the arctic char with the couscous mixture at once. Or cover and refrigerate the fish and couscous separately for up to 8 hours and serve chilled.

PER SERVING (1 piece arctic char and scant 1 cup couscous mixture): 400 Cal, 9 g Fat, 2 g Sat Fat, 0 g Trans Fat, 65 mg Chol, 660 mg Sod, 48 g Carb, 3 g Fib, 30 g Prot, 80 mg Calc. **POINTS** value: **8.**

GOOD IDEA You can use salmon or steelhead trout instead of the arctic char. If you like, sprinkle each serving of couscous with a tablespoon of sliced toasted almonds and increase the **POINTS** value by 1. To save time buy a package of already toasted sliced almonds.

Roast Swordfish with Pepper-Olive Relish

PREP	10 MINUTES
COOK	12 MINUTES
SERVES	4

1 Preheat the oven to 425°F. Spray a baking sheet with olive oil nonstick spray.

2 To make the relish, combine the roasted peppers, olives, basil, vinegar, capers, and garlic in a bowl.

3 Brush the swordfish with the oil and sprinkle with the salt and pepper. Place the swordfish on the sheet. Roast until the swordfish is just opaque in the center, 10–12 minutes. Serve with the relish.

PER SERVING (1 swordfish steak with 3 tablespoons relish): 249 Cal, 11 g Fat, 2 g Sat Fat, 0 g Trans Fat, 62 mg Chol, 669 mg Sod, 5 g Carb, 0 g Fib, 32 g Prot, 15 mg Calc. *POINTS* value: **6.**

GOOD IDEA Halibut fillets work equally well here with the briny olive and sweet pepper relish. Whole-wheat couscous makes a wonderful accompaniment (⅔ cup cooked couscous for each serving will increase the *POINTS* value by 2).

1 (7½-ounce) jar roasted **red bell peppers** (not in oil), drained and finely chopped

8 **niçoise** or **kalamata olives**, pitted and sliced

2 tablespoons chopped **fresh basil**

2 teaspoons **balsamic vinegar**

2 teaspoons drained **capers**

½ small **garlic clove**, minced

4 (6-ounce) **swordfish steaks**, about ¾-inch thick

2 teaspoons **extra-virgin olive oil**

½ teaspoon **salt**

¼ teaspoon freshly **ground pepper**

Roast Swordfish with
Pepper-Olive Relish

Swordfish Mexicana

PREP	20 MINUTES
COOK	ABOUT 15 MINUTES
SERVES	4

1 Preheat the oven to 425°F. Bring 1 inch of water to a boil in a saucepan; add the carrot, onion, corn, and bell peppers. Reduce the heat and simmer, covered, until the vegetables are slightly wilted but still crunchy, about 1 minute; drain.

2 Tear off 4 (12-inch) squares of foil or parchment paper. Place a swordfish steak in the center of each piece; top each with one-fourth of the carrot mixture, the tomatoes, cilantro, jalapeño, salt, and 1 teaspoon of the oil. Fold each piece of foil into a packet, making a tight seal and allowing room for the packets to expand.

3 Transfer the packets to 2 baking sheets and bake 10–12 minutes. Open 1 packet carefully and check the fish, as steam will escape; it should be just opaque in the center. If fish is not fully cooked, reseal the packet and return it to the oven until cooked through. Serve drizzled with any juices and the lime slices.

PER SERVING (1 swordfish steak and ¼ of vegetables): 276 Calories, 10 g Fat, 2 g Sat Fat, 0 g Trans fat, 56 mg Chol, 887 mg Sod, 14 g Carb, 4 g Fib, 31 mg Prot, 46 mg Calc. **POINTS** value: **6.**

1 **carrot**, cut into thin strips

1 **onion**, thinly sliced

½ cup fresh or thawed frozen **corn kernels**

½ **green bell pepper**, seeded and cut into thin strips

½ **red bell pepper**, seeded and cut into thin strips

4 (5-ounce) **swordfish steaks**

1 cup drained **chopped canned tomatoes**

¼ cup minced **fresh cilantro**

1 **jalapeño pepper**, seeded and minced (wear gloves to prevent irritation)

1 teaspoon **salt**

4 teaspoons **canola oil**

4 **lime** slices

Tuna with Corn, Black Beans, and Mango

PREP	15 MINUTES
COOK	ABOUT 5 MINUTES
SERVES	6

1 Combine the lime juice, oil, garlic, oregano, crushed red pepper, and salt in a small bowl.

2 Place the tuna steaks in a shallow glass baking dish. Add 2 tablespoons of the lime juice mixture and turn to coat.

3 Spray a large nonstick skillet with nonstick spray and set over medium-high heat. Add the tuna and cook until browned on the outside but still pink in the center, 2–3 minutes on each side for medium-rare.

4 Meanwhile, combine the beans, corn, mango, bell pepper, onion, cilantro, and the remaining 2 tablespoons lime juice mixture in a medium bowl.

5 Arrange the greens on a serving platter; spoon the bean mixture on top. Arrange the tuna on top of the bean mixture and serve at once.

PER SERVING (1 tuna steak and ⅔ cup salad): 331 Cal, 9 g Fat, 2 g Sat Fat, 0 g Trans Fat, 67 mg Chol, 464 mg Sod, 34 g Carb, 7 g Fib, 30 g Prot, 99 mg Calc. **POINTS** value: **7.**

HOW WE DID IT We recommend not overcooking tuna. For medium tuna, cook it until still slightly rosy in the middle, about 3 minutes on each side. If you prefer your tuna rare, cook it until still bright red in the center, 1–2 minutes on each side. Let the tuna rest for a few minutes before serving—it will continue to cook from the residual heat, but will not dry out.

- 3 tablespoons **fresh lime juice**
- 1 tablespoon **extra-virgin olive oil**
- 1 **garlic clove**, minced
- ½ teaspoon **dried oregano**
- ¼ teaspoon **crushed red pepper**
- ¼ teaspoon **salt**
- 6 (4-ounce) **tuna steaks**
- 1 (15½-ounce) can **black beans**, rinsed and drained
- 1 cup fresh or thawed frozen **corn kernels**
- 1 ripe **mango**, peeled and cut into 1-inch chunks
- 1 **red bell pepper**, seeded and diced
- ½ **red onion**, thinly sliced
- ¼ cup chopped **fresh cilantro**
- 1 (5-ounce) package **spring mix salad greens**

Red Snapper Cakes with
Nectarine-Citrus Salad

Red Snapper Cakes with
Nectarine-Citrus Salad

PREP	20 MINUTES
COOK	ABOUT 10 MINUTES
SERVES	4

1 To make the salad, combine the nectarines, oranges, onion, basil, and lemon juice in a bowl.

2 Combine the snapper, egg, cornmeal, shallot, jalapeño, cilantro, and salt in a bowl. Form into 4 (3-inch) cakes.

3 Heat the oil in a medium nonstick skillet over medium heat. Add the cakes and cook until golden and cooked through, about 5 minutes on each side. Serve with the salad.

PER SERVING (1 snapper cake with 1 cup salad): 281 Cal, 8 g Fat, 1 g Sat Fat, 0 g Trans Fat, 93 mg Chol, 502 mg Sod, 27 g Carb, 4 g Fib, 26 g Prot, 80 mg Calc. **POINTS** value: **5.**

GOOD IDEA If you can't find red snapper or would prefer to use a less expensive fish, tilapia is an excellent substitute. Tilapia, also known as St. Peter's fish, has a slightly denser texture than red snapper but has a similar mild taste.

3 **nectarines**, cut into ¼-inch-thick slices

2 **oranges**, peeled and cut into sections

½ small **red onion**, thinly sliced

3 tablespoons thinly sliced **fresh basil**

1 tablespoon **fresh lemon juice**

1 pound **red snapper fillets**, skinned and finely chopped

1 large **egg**

3 tablespoons **cornmeal**

1 small **shallot**, minced

½ **jalapeño pepper**, seeded and finely chopped (wear gloves to prevent irritation)

2 tablespoons chopped **fresh cilantro**

¾ teaspoon **salt**

4 teaspoons **olive oil**

Snapper with Cilantro Sauce

PREP	15 MINUTES
COOK	ABOUT 15 MINUTES
SERVES	4

3 cups loosely packed **fresh cilantro** leaves

¼ cup **water**

1 tablespoon **olive oil**

1 tablespoon **fresh lime juice**

¼ teaspoon grated **lime zest**

1 **serrano pepper**, seeded and minced (wear gloves to prevent irritation)

¼ teaspoon **salt**

4 (6-ounce) **red snapper fillets**, skinned

1 Preheat the oven to 400ºF. To make the cilantro sauce, puree the cilantro, water, oil, lime juice, lime zest, serrano, and salt in a blender.

2 Spray 4 (12-inch) squares of foil with olive oil nonstick spray. Place a fillet on the center of each piece; spread each with one-quarter of the cilantro sauce (about 2 tablespoons). Fold each piece of foil into a packet, making a tight seal allowing room for the packets to expand. Transfer the packets to a baking sheet. Bake until the snapper is just opaque in the center, 13–15 minutes. Open the packets carefully when testing for doneness, as steam will escape.

PER SERVING (1 fillet): 198 Cal, 6 g Fat, 1 g Sat Fat, 0 g Trans Fat, 60 mg Chol, 224 mg Sod, 1 g Carb, 0 g Fib, 34 g Prot, 60 mg Calc. *POINTS* value: *4.*

DEFINITION Small, slender serrano (seh-RRAH-noh) chiles have a very hot, savory flavor and can be found in Mexican markets and larger supermarkets. Or substitute half a milder jalapeño pepper, seeded and minced.

Thai Monkfish Stir-Fry

PREP	10 MINUTES
COOK	ABOUT 10 MINUTES
SERVES	4

1 Heat the oil in a large nonstick skillet over medium-high heat. Add the garlic and curry powder. Cook, stirring frequently, until fragrant, about 30 seconds. Add the broccoli, bell peppers, and scallions; cook, stirring occasionally, until crisp-tender, about 5 minutes.

2 Add the corn, coconut milk, fish sauce, and ginger to the skillet; bring to a simmer, stirring occasionally. Gently stir in the monkfish. Reduce the heat and simmer, uncovered, until the fish is just opaque in the center, about 5 minutes.

PER SERVING (1⅓ cups): 282 Cal, 10 g Fat, 4 g Sat Fat, 0 g Trans Fat, 62 mg Chol, 409 mg Sod, 27 g Carb, 7 g Fib, 29 g Prot, 86 mg Calc. **POINTS** value: **6.**

FOOD NOTE You can find red curry powder in the gourmet spice section of the supermarket and coconut milk, fish sauce, and bottled sliced ginger in the ethnic food section.

2 teaspoons **canola oil**

2 **garlic cloves**, minced

1–2 teaspoons **red curry powder**

1 (12-ounce) bag fresh **broccoli florets**, halved

2 **red bell peppers**, seeded and cut into 1-inch pieces

5 **scallions**, cut into 1-inch pieces

1 cup frozen **corn kernels**

1 cup light (reduced-fat) **coconut milk**

2 tablespoons **Asian fish sauce** (nam pla) or reduced-sodium soy sauce

1 tablespoon chopped, drained **bottled sliced ginger**

1 pound **monkfish fillets**, cut into 1-inch pieces

Microwave Herbed Cod
with Tomato Sauce

PREP	10 MINUTES
COOK	ABOUT 15 MINUTES
SERVES	4

1 Heat 1 teaspoon of the oil in a medium nonstick skillet over medium heat. Add the onion and cook, stirring occasionally, until softened, 2–3 minutes. Stir in half the garlic and cook 30 seconds. Add the tomatoes and thyme; cook until the flavors are blended, 2–3 minutes. Remove the skillet from the heat; cover and keep warm.

2 Spray a shallow microwavable dish with olive oil nonstick spray; place the cod in the dish. Combine the parsley, the remaining 1 tablespoon oil, half the garlic, the salt, and pepper in a small bowl; spread over the cod. Cover the dish with wax paper and microwave on High until the cod is just opaque in the center, 6–7 minutes. Spread tomato sauce on serving platter; arrange the cod on top.

PER SERVING (1 piece cod with 5 tablespoons sauce): 194 Cal, 6 g Fat, 1 g Sat Fat, 0 g Trans Fat, 65 mg Chol, 614 mg Sod, 6 g Carb, 1 g Fib, 28 g Prot, 43 mg Calc. **POINTS** value: **4.**

GOOD IDEA You can also use a 14½-ounce can diced tomatoes for the sauce. Add as directed in Step 1, but increase the heat and cook until the sauce thickens, 5 to 8 minutes.

1 teaspoon + 1 tablespoon **extra-virgin olive oil**

½ small **onion**, finely chopped

2 **garlic cloves**, minced

1 (14½ -ounce) can **fire-roasted crushed tomatoes**

¼ teaspoon **dried thyme**

1½ pounds **cod fillet**, 1 inch thick, skinned and cut into 4 pieces

3 tablespoons chopped fresh **flat-leaf parsley**

½ teaspoon **salt**

¼ teaspoon freshly **ground pepper**

Garlicky Fish and Bread Soup

PREP	5 MINUTES
COOK	ABOUT 15 MINUTES
SERVES	4

1 teaspoon **olive oil**

1 **onion**, chopped

4 cups bottled **clam juice,** or fish or vegetable broth

2 tablespoons **dry vermouth**

1 pound skinless **cod, halibut**, or **flounder fillets**, cut into 1-inch pieces

1 (6-ounce) bag **arugula** leaves

¾ teaspoon **dried thyme**

2 tablespoons **low-fat mayonnaise**

2 **garlic cloves**, minced

4 ounces **whole-wheat Italian bread**, cut into cubes (about 4 cups)

1 Heat the oil in a nonstick Dutch oven over medium-high heat. Add the onion and cook, stirring occasionally, until golden, about 5 minutes. Add the clam juice and vermouth; bring to a boil. Add the cod, arugula, and thyme; return to a boil, stirring occasionally to incorporate the arugula. Reduce the heat and simmer until the fish is just opaque in the center and the arugula is wilted, about 3 minutes.

2 Meanwhile, combine the mayonnaise and garlic in a small bowl. Stir about ¼ cup of the hot broth into the mayonnaise mixture; whisk until smooth. Return the mayonnaise mixture to the Dutch oven, stirring constantly until blended and heated through, about 1 minute.

3 Place 1 cup of the bread cubes in the bottom of each of 4 soup bowls. Ladle a scant 2 cups of the soup over the bread in each bowl.

PER SERVING (1 bowl soup): 273 Cal, 7 g Fat, 1 g Sat Fat, 0 g Trans Fat, 70 mg Chol, 882 mg Sod, 24 g Carb, 4 g Fib, 28 g Prot, 156 mg Calc. ***POINTS*** value: *5.*

Sicilian Cod with Zucchini

PREP	5 MINUTES
COOK	ABOUT 15 MINUTES
SERVES	4

2 teaspoons **olive oil**

1 **onion**, chopped

2 **garlic cloves**, minced

1 (14½-ounce) can **crushed tomatoes**

1 medium **zucchini**, diced (about 2 cups)

8 pitted **kalamata olives**, halved

2 canned **anchovy fillets**, rinsed, drained, and chopped

1 tablespoon drained **capers**

¼ teaspoon **crushed red pepper**

1½ pounds **cod fillet**, cut into 4 pieces

1 Heat the oil in a large nonstick skillet over medium-high heat. Add the onion and garlic; cook, stirring frequently, until softened, about 3 minutes.

2 Add the tomatoes, zucchini, olives, anchovies, capers, and crushed red pepper; bring to a boil, stirring occasionally. Reduce the heat and simmer, uncovered, about 4 minutes.

3 Add the cod to the skillet, spooning some of the tomato mixture over the fish. Cover and simmer until the fish is just opaque in the center, about 7 minutes.

PER SERVING (1 piece cod with ½ cup vegetables and sauce): 227 Cal, 6 g Fat, 1 g Sat Fat, 0 g Trans Fat, 91 mg Chol, 457 mg Sod, 10 g Carb, 2 g Fib, 35 g Prot, 80 mg Calc. **POINTS** value: **5.**

GOOD IDEA Serve this robust dish with cooked orzo (½ cup will up the **POINTS** value by 2).

Sicilian Cod with Zucchini

Catfish Florentine en Papillote

PREP	10 MINUTES
COOK	ABOUT 10 MINUTES
SERVES	4

1 Preheat the oven to 550°F. Cut 4 (12 x 20-inch) sheets of parchment paper or foil.

2 Divide the spinach among the 4 sheets of parchment; top each with a fish fillet. Sprinkle evenly with the feta cheese, olives, lemon zest, lemon juice, oregano, and pepper.

3 Fold the parchment over the fish, making a tight seal. Make packets by bringing the sides of the parchment up to meet in the center and folding over the edges, then folding the edges of the ends together. Allowing room for the packets to expand, crimp the edges.

4 Place the parchment parcels on a large baking sheet and bake until the fish is just opaque in the center, about 10 minutes. Transfer the parcels to plates and open them with care to avoid getting a steam burn.

PER SERVING (1 parcel): 209 Cal, 10 g Fat, 3 g Sat Fat, 0 g Trans Fat, 94 mg Chol, 237 mg Sod, 3 g Carb, 2 g Fib, 26 g Prot, 150 mg Calc. **POINTS** value: **5.**

EXPRESS LANE While they need to be baked at the last minute, these fish parcels can be assembled several hours ahead and kept in the refrigerator until you are ready to bake them.

- 1 (6-ounce) bag **baby spinach trio** (baby spinach, arugula, and carrots)
- 4 (¼-pound) skinless **catfish fillets**
- ¼ cup crumbled **feta cheese**
- 2 tablespoons chopped pitted **kalamata olives**
- 1 teaspoon grated **lemon zest**
- 2 tablespoons **fresh lemon juice**
- 1 teaspoon **dried oregano**
- ¼ teaspoon freshly **ground pepper**

Cabbage-Wrapped Halibut

PREP	15 MINUTES PLUS 5 MINUTES COOLING TIME
COOK	ABOUT 30 MINUTES
SERVES	4

4 large **green cabbage leaves**

2 tablespoons **fresh lemon juice**

2 tablespoons reduced-sodium **soy sauce**

4 (6-ounce) **halibut fillets**, skinned

1 (1-inch) piece **fresh ginger**, peeled and cut into very thin strips

2 teaspoons **flaxseed oil**

1 Bring a large saucepan of lightly salted water to a boil. Add the cabbage and return to a boil. Cook until the cabbage is pliable, about 3 minutes. With tongs, transfer the cabbage to a bowl and cool 5 minutes. Discard all but 1 inch of water from the saucepan.

2 Combine the lemon juice and soy sauce in a bowl. Place 1 halibut fillet onto the center of each cabbage leaf. Top each with one-fourth of the ginger and drizzle each with 1 tablespoon of the lemon mixture. Fold in the sides of each leaf to cover the fillets and secure with a toothpick.

3 Return the water to a boil in the saucepan. Put the rolls, seam-side up, in a steamer basket; set in the saucepan. Cover tightly and steam until the cabbage is very soft and the fish feels firm to the touch, about 12 minutes. Open the rolls carefully, as steam will escape. Serve, sprinkling each fillet with ½ teaspoon of the oil.

PER SERVING (1 roll): 203 Cal, 5 g Fat, 0 g Sat Fat, 0 g Trans Fat, 53 mg Chol, 400 mg Sod, 3 g Carb, 1 g Fib, 36 g Prot, 77 mg Calc. **POINTS** value: **4.**

FOOD NOTE Flaxseed oil is highly perishable, so be sure to check the sell-by date when purchasing and keep it refrigerated up to 3 months. Flaxseed oil should not be exposed to direct heat, as in sautéeing, which will damage the oil. So enjoy its mild nutty flavor drizzled over cooked foods or in salads.

Crispy Cornmeal Flounder

Crispy Cornmeal Flounder

PREP	10 MINUTES
COOK	ABOUT 12 MINUTES
SERVES	4

1 Combine the cornmeal, parsley, oregano, Cajun seasoning, and salt on a large plate. Combine the egg whites and mustard in a large bowl; mix well.

2 Dip 1 flounder fillet in the egg white mixture, then in the cornmeal mixture, pressing gently to coat. Place the fillet on a plate; repeat with the remaining fillets.

3 Heat 2 teaspoons of oil in a large nonstick skillet over medium-high heat. Add 2 fillets and cook, until golden and the fish is just opaque in the center, about 3 minutes on each side. Transfer the fillets to a platter. Repeat with the remaining 2 teaspoons oil and 2 fillets. Serve with the salsa.

PER SERVING (1 fillet with 2 tablespoons salsa): 283 Cal, 8 g Fat, 1 g Sat Fat, 0 g Trans Fat, 80 mg Chol, 987 mg Sod, 19 g Carb, 3 g Fib, 34 g Prot, 62 mg Calc. **POINTS** value: **6.**

EXPRESS LANE Use an extra-large (at least 12-inch) skillet to cook the flounder fillets in one go and shave off about 6 minutes from this recipe.

½ cup **yellow cornmeal**

¼ cup chopped **fresh parsley**

1 tablespoon chopped **fresh oregano**

2 teaspoons **Cajun seasoning**

½ teaspoon **salt**

2 **egg whites**, lightly beaten

3 tablespoons **Dijon mustard**

4 (6-ounce) **flounder** or **sole fillets**, skinned

4 teaspoons **olive oil**

½ cup **mild fat-free salsa**

Roasted Halibut with Lemon Dressing

PREP	10 MINUTES PLUS 10 MINUTES STANDING TIME
COOK	ABOUT 15 MINUTES
SERVES	4

1 Preheat the oven to 450°F. Spray a large shallow baking dish with olive oil nonstick spray.

2 Meanwhile, combine the lemon juice, soy sauce, ginger, garlic, mustard, thyme, and crushed red pepper in a small bowl. Gradually whisk in the oil until blended. Place the halibut in the baking dish; add the lemon dressing, turning to coat. Let stand 10 minutes.

3 Sprinkle the halibut with the salt. Roast until the halibut is just opaque in the center, 14–16 minutes.

PER SERVING (¼ of halibut): 209 Cal, 7 g Fat, 1 g Sat Fat, 0 g Trans Fat, 53 mg Chol, 565 mg Sod, 3 g Carb, 0 g Fib, 36 g Prot, 70 mg Calc.
POINTS value: **5.**

¼ cup **fresh lemon juice**

1 tablespoon reduced-sodium **soy sauce**

1 tablespoon minced peeled **fresh ginger**

2 **garlic cloves**, minced

1 teaspoon **Dijon mustard**

½ teaspoon **dried thyme**

¼ teaspoon **crushed red pepper**

1 tablespoon **olive oil**

1½ pounds **halibut fillet**, about 1¼ inches thick, skinned

½ teaspoon **salt**

Shrimp Diavolo

PREP	15 MINUTES
COOK	ABOUT 25 MINUTES
SERVES	4

1 Sprinkle the shrimp with ½ teaspoon of the salt. Heat 2 teaspoons of the oil in a large nonstick skillet over medium-high heat. Add half the shrimp and cook until golden and just opaque in the center, about 2 minutes on each side. Transfer the shrimp to a plate with a slotted spoon. Repeat with the remaining shrimp.

2 Heat the remaining 2 teaspoons oil in the same skillet over medium heat. Add the garlic, oregano, and crushed red pepper; cook, stirring constantly, until fragrant, about 30 seconds. Stir in the tomatoes and tomato paste; cook until slightly thickened, 4–6 minutes. Add the shrimp and the remaining ¼ teaspoon salt; cook, stirring occasionally, until heated through, about 1 minute.

3 Meanwhile, cook the linguine according to package directions; drain in a colander. Divide the linguine among 4 plates, and top each serving with the sauce.

PER SERVING (about 1 cup pasta with about ½ cup sauce): 367 Cal, 7 g Fat, 1 g Sat Fat, 0 g Trans Fat, 168 mg Chol, 782 mg Sod, 52 g Carb, 10 g Fib, 29 g Prot, 102 mg Calc. **POINTS** value: **7.**

GOOD IDEA To make this a more family-friendly dish, omit the crushed red pepper or cut to ⅛ teaspoon. The sauce will be equally hearty and satisfying.

1 pound large **shrimp**, peeled and deveined

¾ teaspoon **salt**

4 teaspoons **extra-virgin olive oil**

2 **garlic cloves**, minced

1 teaspoon **dried oregano**

¼ teaspoon **crushed red pepper**

1 (15-ounce) **can crushed tomatoes**

3 tablespoons **tomato paste**

½ pound **whole-wheat linguine** or **spaghetti**

Mediterranean Shrimp and Scallop Salad

PREP	20 MINUTES
COOK	ABOUT 15 MINUTES
SERVES	4

1 Bring a medium saucepan two-thirds full of water to a gentle simmer. Add the shrimp and cook until just opaque in the center, about 2 minutes. With a slotted spoon, transfer the shrimp to a bowl filled with ice water. Return the water to a simmer; add the scallops and cook until just opaque in the center, about 2 minutes. With a slotted spoon, transfer the scallops to the bowl with the shrimp.

2 Drain the shrimp and scallops; transfer to a large bowl. Add the fennel, celery, onion, tomatoes, basil, oil, vinegar, oregano, salt, and pepper; mix well.

PER SERVING (1¾ cups): 224 Cal, 6 g Fat, 1 g Sat Fat, 0 g Trans Fat, 168 mg Chol, 810 mg Sod, 8 g Carb, 2 g Fib, 31 g Prot, 69 mg Calc. *POINTS* value: **5.**

GOOD IDEA If tiny bay scallops aren't available, use ¾ pound of sea scallops, but cut each into quarters. Serve the salad on a bed of mesclun.

☑

¾ pound peeled and deveined medium **shrimp**

¾ pound **bay scallops**

1 small **fennel bulb,** quartered and very thinly sliced

1 **celery** stalk, thinly sliced

½ small **red onion,** thinly sliced

1 pint **cherry tomatoes,** halved

¼ cup chopped **fresh basil**

4 teaspoons **extra-virgin olive oil**

1 tablespoon **red-wine vinegar**

½ teaspoon **dried oregano**

¾ teaspoon **salt**

¼ teaspoon freshly **ground pepper**

Mediterranean Shrimp and Scallop Salad

Spicy Shrimp Fried Rice

PREP	10 MINUTES
COOK	ABOUT 10 MINUTES
SERVES	4

2 teaspoons canola oil

2 large eggs, lightly beaten

6 scallions, sliced

1 tablespoon minced peeled fresh ginger

2 cups cold cooked brown rice

1 cup frozen petite peas

2 tablespoons reduced-sodium soy sauce

2 teaspoons seasoned rice vinegar

¼–½ teaspoon crushed red pepper

¾ pound cooked small-medium shrimp

1 Heat 1 teaspoon of the oil in a large nonstick skillet over medium-high heat. Add the eggs and cook, stirring occasionally, until scrambled and cooked through, about 2 minutes. Transfer to a plate.

2 Heat the remaining 1 teaspoon oil in the same skillet. Add the scallions and ginger; cook, stirring frequently, until fragrant, about 30 seconds. Add the rice, peas, soy sauce, vinegar, and crushed red pepper; cook, stirring occasionally, until heated through, about 4 minutes.

3 Add the shrimp and egg; cook, stirring occasionally, until heated through, about 3 minutes.

PER SERVING (generous 1 cup): 267 Cal, 7 g Fat, 1 g Sat Fat, 0 g Trans Fat, 227 mg Chol, 467 mg Sod, 30 g Carb, 5 g Fib, 21 g Prot, 72 mg Calc. **POINTS** value: **5.**

GOOD IDEA For extra flavor, stir in 1½ teaspoons Asian (dark) sesame oil with the shrimp and egg and deduct it from your weekly **POINTS** Allowance (1½ teaspoons oil will increase the per-serving **POINTS** value by ½).

Bouillabaisse

PREP	20 MINUTES PLUS 5 MINUTES STANDING TIME
COOK	ABOUT 55 MINUTES
SERVES	4

1 Bring the potatoes and enough cold water to cover by 2 inches to a boil in a medium saucepan; cook 5 minutes. Remove the pan from the heat. Let the potatoes stand until just tender but hold their shape, about 5 minutes. Drain.

2 Meanwhile, cut the fennel in half. Chop one half and cut the other half into 8 wedges.

3 Heat the oil in a large saucepan over medium heat. Add the chopped fennel, the tomatoes, garlic, and saffron; cook, stirring occasionally, until the fennel is softened, about 7 minutes. Stir in the clam juice. Increase the heat to medium-high and bring to a boil. Reduce the heat and simmer until reduced by one-quarter (about 2½ cups), about 20 minutes. Strain the clam mixture through a sieve into a bowl, pressing down on the solids with a wooden spoon. Discard the solids.

4 Return the broth to the pan. Add the fennel wedges and simmer until crisp-tender, about 4 minutes. Transfer the fennel with a slotted spoon to a platter. Add the salmon and simmer until the fish is just opaque in the center, about 7 minutes. Transfer the salmon with a slotted spoon to the same platter. Add the cod and simmer until the fish is just opaque in the center, about 7 minutes. Transfer the cod with a slotted spoon to the platter. Add the shrimp and simmer until just opaque in the center, about 2 minutes. Transfer the shrimp with a slotted spoon to the platter.

5 Divide the potatoes among 4 shallow bowls. Add 2 fennel wedges, 1 piece salmon, 1 piece cod, and one-fourth of the shrimp to each bowl. Divide the broth among the bowls and serve at once.

PER SERVING (about 2 cups): 297 Cal, 7 g Fat, 1 g Sat Fat, 0 g Trans Fat, 143 mg Chol, 577 mg Sod, 24 g Carb, 4 g Fib, 34 g Prot, 95 mg Calc.
POINTS value: **6.**

¾ pound **red potatoes**, cut into ½-inch cubes

1 large **fennel bulb**

1 tablespoon **extra-virgin olive oil**

½ pound **plum tomatoes**, chopped

2 **garlic cloves**, minced

¼ teaspoon **saffron threads**, lightly crushed

3 (8-ounce) bottles **clam juice**

1 (½-pound) **salmon fillet**, skinned and cut into 4 pieces

1 (½-pound) **cod fillet**, skinned and cut into 4 pieces

½ pound peeled and deveined extra-large **shrimp**

Pan-Seared Scallops
with Melon Salsa

Pan-Seared Scallops with Melon Salsa

PREP	10 MINUTES
COOK	ABOUT 12 MINUTES
SERVES	4

1 To make the salsa, combine the cantaloupe, honeydew, onion, serrano, cilantro, mint, and lemon juice in a bowl.

2 Sprinkle the scallops with the salt and pepper. Heat 2 teaspoons of the oil in a large nonstick skillet over medium-high heat. Add half of the scallops and cook until browned and just opaque in the center, about 3 minutes on each side. Transfer the scallops to a plate. Repeat with the remaining 2 teaspoons oil and scallops. Serve with the salsa.

PER SERVING (about ½ cup scallops with ½ cup salsa): 262 Cal, 6 g Fat, 1 g Sat Fat, 0 g Trans Fat, 84 mg Chol, 844 mg Sod, 13 g Carb, 1 g Fib, 34 g Prot, 45 mg Calc. **POINTS** value: **6.**

HOW WE DID IT While completely edible, a number of the scallops may have a tough muscle attached to a side, which you might like to remove. Simply pull the muscle from the scallop with your fingers.

¼ **cantaloupe**, peeled and diced

¼ **honeydew melon**, peeled and diced

3 tablespoons finely chopped **red onion**

½ **serrano pepper**, seeded and minced (wear gloves to prevent irritation)

1 tablespoon chopped **fresh cilantro**

1 tablespoon chopped **fresh mint**

1 tablespoon **fresh lemon juice**

1½ pounds **sea scallops**

¾ teaspoon **salt**

¼ teaspoon freshly **ground pepper**

4 teaspoons **olive oil**

CHAPTER 7

Go Meatless

Tofu, Asparagus, and Mushroom "Risotto"

PREP	**10 MINUTES PLUS 5 MINUTES STANDING TIME**
COOK	**ABOUT 50 MINUTES**
SERVES	**4**

1 Bring the broth to a simmer in a medium saucepan over medium heat.

2 Meanwhile, heat 2 teaspoons of the oil in a large nonstick skillet over medium-high heat. Add the tofu and cook, stirring occasionally, until lightly browned, about 5 minutes. Transfer the tofu to a plate.

3 Heat 1 teaspoon of the oil in the same skillet over medium-high heat. Add the mushrooms and salt; cook, stirring occasionally, until the mushrooms have released their liquid and are lightly browned, about 4 minutes. Add the asparagus and cook until starting to soften and turn bright green, about 3 minutes. Transfer the vegetables to the plate with the tofu.

4 Heat the remaining 1 teaspoon oil in the same skillet over medium-high heat. Add the shallot and cook, stirring frequently, until fragrant, about 30 seconds. Add the rice and lemon juice; cook, stirring constantly, until the juice evaporates, about 30 seconds. Add ½ cup of the hot broth and cook, stirring constantly, until the liquid is almost completely absorbed, about 1 minute. Add the remaining 2½ cups broth and bring to a boil. Reduce the heat and simmer, covered, until the rice is almost tender, about 30 minutes (there should be quite a bit of liquid remaining in the skillet). Uncover, increase the heat to medium-high, and bring to a boil. Cook until the liquid is almost completely absorbed, about 3 minutes. Add the tofu and vegetables; cook, stirring occasionally, until heated through, about 1 minute. Let stand 5 minutes before serving.

PER SERVING (1¼ cups): 198 Cal, 7 g Fat, 1 g Sat Fat, 0 g Trans Fat, 0 mg Chol, 975 mg Sod, 26 g Carb, 2 g Fib, 11 g Prot, 53 mg Calc.
POINTS value: *4.*

3 cups **vegetable broth**

4 teaspoons **extra-virgin olive oil**

1 (12.3-ounce) container **reduced-fat firm tofu**, drained well and cut into ½-inch cubes

1 (8-ounce) package sliced **fresh mushrooms**

¼ teaspoon **salt**

½ pound **fresh asparagus**, trimmed and cut into 1-inch pieces

1 **shallot**, chopped

¾ cup quick-cooking **brown rice**

1 tablespoon **fresh lemon juice**

Tofu, Asparagus, and Mushroom "Risotto"

Quick Soy Burritos

PREP	5 MINUTES
COOK	ABOUT 10 MINUTES
SERVES	4

1 Prepare the rice according to package directions, omitting the salt; keep warm.

2 Meanwhile, heat the oil in a large nonstick skillet over high heat. Add the onion, garlic, and jalapeño; cook, stirring, until softened, about 4 minutes. Add the soy crumbles, chili powder, and cumin; cook, stirring, until hot, about 3 minutes. Stir in the rice and salt and cook 1 minute more.

3 Warm the tortillas according to package directions, then spoon one-fourth of rice mixture, 3 tablespoons salsa, and 1 tablespoon sour cream onto each. Roll up and serve at once.

PER SERVING (1 burrito): 390 Cal, 5 g Fat, 1 g Sat Fat, 0 g Trans Fat, 0 mg Chol, 988 mg Sod, 65 g Carb, 7 g Fib, 22 g Prot, 114 mg Calc. **POINTS** value: **7.**

DEFINITION Soy protein crumbles, sometimes labeled "meatless ground burger" or "recipe grillers," are available in your supermarket's frozen foods section. They provide a healthy helping of protein.

¾ cup quick-cooking **brown rice**

2 teaspoons **olive oil**

1 **onion**, chopped

2 **garlic cloves**, minced

1 **jalapeño pepper**, seeded and finely chopped (wear gloves to prevent irritation)

1½ cups frozen **soy protein crumbles**

1 teaspoon **chili powder**

½ teaspoon **ground cumin**

½ teaspoon **salt**

4 (8-inch) **fat-free flour tortillas**

¾ cup **salsa**

4 tablespoons **fat-free sour cream**

Tempeh-Cashew Stir-Fry

PREP	5 MINUTES
COOK	ABOUT 10 MINUTES
SERVES	4

¾ cup quick-cooking **brown rice**

1 cup **vegetable broth**

¼ cup **hoisin sauce**

1 tablespoon reduced-sodium **soy sauce**

2 teaspoons **cornstarch**

3 teaspoon **peanut oil**

6 ounces **tempeh**, cut into ½-inch cubes (about 1 cup)

5 **scallions**, chopped

1 tablespoon grated **fresh ginger**

1 (12-ounce) bag fresh pre-cut **vegetables** for stir-fry (try broccoli, carrots, and snow peas)

2 tablespoons coarsely chopped **unsalted cashews**

1 Prepare the rice according to package directions, omitting the salt; keep warm.

2 Meanwhile, stir together the broth, hoisin sauce, soy sauce, and cornstarch in a small bowl; set aside.

3 Heat a large nonstick skillet or wok over high heat until a drop of water sizzles. Pour in 1½ teaspoons of the oil and swirl to coat the pan. Add the tempeh and stir-fry until lightly browned, about 3 minutes. Transfer the tempeh to a plate.

4 Heat the remaining 1½ teaspoons oil in the wok. Add the scallions and ginger; stir-fry until fragrant, about 30 seconds. Add the vegetables and stir-fry until just crisp-tender, about 3 minutes. Stir in the cashews and heat through, about 1 minute. Add the broth mixture and cook, stirring constantly, until thickened, about 1 minute. Add the tempeh and heat through, stirring gently, about 1 minute. Serve over the rice.

PER SERVING (scant ½ cup rice and 1 cup vegetable mixture): 346 Cal, 12 g Fat, 2 g Sat Fat, 0 g Trans Fat, 0 mg Chol, 859 mg Sod, 48 g Carb, 9 g Fib, 15 g Prot, 110 mg Calc. *POINTS* value: *7.*

DEFINITION Tempeh (TEHM-pay) is a fermented soybean cake high in protein, with a nutty flavor and a chewy texture similar to brown rice. Look for it the refrigerated organics section of your supermarket, or at natural food stores. If you can't find it, substitute pressed, cubed extra-firm tofu.

Polenta with Veggie Burger Tomato Sauce

PREP	10 MINUTES
COOK	ABOUT 15 MINUTES
SERVES	4

1 Heat the oil in a large nonstick skillet over medium-high heat. Add the onion, garlic, and fennel seeds; cook, stirring occasionally, until slightly softened, about 2 minutes. Stir in the vegetable burgers and cook, stirring occasionally, until browned, about 3 minutes. Reduce the heat; add the tomatoes and tomato paste. Simmer, covered, until the sauce starts to thicken, about 10 minutes.

2 Meanwhile, combine the milk, water, salt, and pepper in a medium saucepan; bring to a boil over medium-high heat. Slowly pour in the polenta in a thin, steady stream whisking constantly. Cook, whisking constantly, until thick and creamy, about 5 minutes. Remove the saucepan from the heat; stir in the cheese. Divide the polenta among 4 plates; top each serving with the tomato sauce.

PER SERVING (1 cup polenta and ½ cup sauce): 379 Cal, 5 g Fat, 1 g Sat Fat, 0 g Trans Fat, 14 mg Chol, 1,136 mg Sod, 57 g Carb, 8 g Fib, 27 g Prot, 372 mg Calc. **POINTS** value: **7.**

HOW WE DID IT Allow the frozen burgers to stand at room temperature about 10 minutes to soften slightly and they'll be easier to chop.

2 teaspoons **olive oil**

1 **onion**, chopped

3 **garlic cloves**, minced

½ teaspoon **fennel seeds**

2 frozen **grilled vegetable burgers**, chopped into small pieces

1 (14½-ounce) **can whole tomatoes**, chopped

3 tablespoons **tomato paste**

3 cups **fat-free milk**

1 cup **water**

1 teaspoon **salt**

¼ teaspoon freshly **ground pepper**

¾ cup instant **polenta**

1 cup **fat-free ricotta cheese**

Portobello, Mozzarella, and Roasted Red Pepper Subs

PREP	5 MINUTES
COOK	ABOUT 10 MINUTES
SERVES	4

1 Preheat broiler. Spray a baking sheet with nonstick spray.

2 Whisk together the vinegar, oil, basil, salt, and ground pepper in a small bowl; set aside.

3 Brush both sides of the mushroom caps with ½ of the vinegar mixture and arrange on the baking sheet. Broil 4 inches from the heat until tender and browned, about 3 minutes on each side.

4 Arrange the bottom halves of the rolls on the baking sheet and top each with a mushroom, 1 roasted pepper piece, 1 onion slice, and 1 cheese slice. Broil until the cheese melts and browns slightly, about 1 minute. Brush the cut sides of the top halves of the rolls with the remaining vinegar mixture and place over the cheese. Serve warm, at room temperature, or chilled.

PER SERVING (1 sandwich): 308 Cal, 8 g Fat, 1 g Sat Fat, 0 g Trans Fat, 3 mg Chol, 815 mg Sod, 47 g Carb, 4 g Fib, 14 g Prot, 194 mg Calc.
POINTS value: **6.**

GOOD IDEA These easy-fix sandwiches are delicious right out of the oven, but they're even better a day later—making them a terrific brown-bag lunch. Wrap them individually in plastic wrap and refrigerate overnight, giving the flavors time to mellow and blend.

2 tablespoons **balsamic vinegar**

1½ tablespoons **extra-virgin olive oil**

1 teaspoon **dried basil**

¼ teaspoon **salt**

¼ teaspoon freshly **ground pepper**

4 fresh **portobello mushrooms** (about 1 pound), stems removed

4 (2½-ounce) **sub rolls**, halved horizontally

1 jarred roasted **red bell pepper**, cut into 4 pieces

½ small **red onion**, cut into 4 slices

4 (½-ounce) slices **fat-free mozzarella cheese**

Mushroom, Onion, and
Pepperjack Quesadillas

Mushroom, Onion, and Pepperjack Quesadillas

PREP	5 MINUTES
COOK	ABOUT 15 MINUTES
SERVES	4

1 teaspoon **olive oil**

2 **onions**, thinly sliced

2 cups sliced fresh **white mushrooms**

2 **garlic cloves**, minced

1 teaspoon **sugar**

½ teaspoon **salt**

½ cup frozen or drained canned **corn kernels**

1 tablespoon chopped **fresh cilantro**

4 (8-inch) **fat-free flour tortillas**

¾ cup shredded **pepperjack cheese**

1 Heat the oil in a large nonstick skillet over high heat. Add the onions, mushrooms, garlic, sugar, and salt; cook, stirring, until the vegetables start to soften, about 3 minutes. Add the corn and cook, stirring frequently, until the mushrooms are tender and the onions brown slightly, about 5 minutes. Transfer the mixture to a bowl and stir in the cilantro.

2 Arrange the tortillas on a work surface and spread the lower half of each with ½ cup of the onion mixture. Sprinkle each with 3 tablespoons of the cheese. Fold the top half of the tortilla over the filling and press lightly.

3 Wipe out the skillet with a paper towel and return it tohigh heat. Add 2 quesadillas to the skillet and cook until the cheese melts and the tortillas are lightly browned, about 1 minute on each side. Repeat with the 2 remaining quesadillas.

PER SERVING (1 quesadilla): 289 Cal, 8 g Fat, 4 g Sat Fat, 0 g Trans Fat, 19 mg Chol, 876 mg Sod, 43 g Carb, 3 g Fib, 12 g Prot, 225 mg Calc.
POINTS value: **6.**

GOOD IDEA If you aren't a fan of spicy foods, you can substitute shredded Monterey Jack or sharp cheddar cheese for the pepperjack.

Greek Pizza

PREP	10 MINUTES
COOK	ABOUT 10 MINUTES
SERVES	4

1 Preheat the oven to 450°F.

2 Meanwhile, place the pizza crust on a baking sheet and top with the pasta sauce, leaving a ½-inch border around the edge. Top evenly with the tomatoes, mushrooms, scallions, cheese, and capers. Bake until the cheese melts slightly and the crust is crisp, about 10 minutes.

PER SERVING (¼ of pizza): 287 Cal, 7 g Fat, 2 g Sat Fat, 0 g Trans Fat, 10 mg Chol, 963 mg Sod, 45 g Carb, 3 g Fib, 11 g Prot, 164 mg Calc.
POINTS value: **6.**

1 (10-ounce) pre-baked thin **pizza crust**

1 cup (from a 26-ounce jar) fat-free **garlic-herb tomato sauce**

2 **plum tomatoes**, thinly sliced

1 cup sliced fresh **white mushrooms**

2 **scallions**, chopped

¾ cup crumbled **reduced-fat feta cheese**

2 teaspoons drained **capers**

Salad Pizzas

PREP	10 MINUTES
COOK	ABOUT 5 MINUTES
SERVES	4

1 Preheat the oven to 450°F.

2 Meanwhile, toss together the lettuce, tomatoes, artichoke hearts, beans, roasted peppers, onion, vinegar, oil, and ground pepper in a medium bowl. Arrange the tortillas in a single layer on 2 baking sheets. Top each with 1 ¼ cups of the salad, then sprinkle each with one-fourth of the cheese. Bake until the cheese melts and the lettuce has wilted slightly, about 5 minutes.

PER SERVING (1 pizza): 330 Cal, 6 g Fat, 1 g Sat Fat, 0 g Trans Fat, 3 mg Chol, 957 mg Sod, 55 g Carb, 9 g Fib, 15 g Prot, 232 mg Calc.
POINTS value: **6.**

GOOD IDEA For delicious flavor and an extra ½ **POINTS** value per serving, sprinkle the pizzas with 12 sliced, pitted large kalamata olives.

3 cups chopped **romaine lettuce** (about ½ medium head)

½ pint **cherry tomatoes**, halved

1 (8½-ounce) can quartered **artichoke hearts**, drained

1 cup rinsed and drained canned **red kidney beans**

1 (7-ounce) jar roasted **red bell peppers**, drained and sliced

½ small **red onion**, thinly sliced

2 tablespoons **balsamic vinegar**

1½ tablespoons **extra-virgin olive oil**

¼ teaspoon freshly **ground pepper**

4 (8-inch) **fat-free flour tortillas**

½ cup shredded **fat-free mozzarella cheese**

Frittata with Sun-Dried Tomatoes, Chard, and Leeks

PREP	**20 MINUTES PLUS 10 MINUTES STANDING TIME**
COOK	**ABOUT 20 MINUTES**
SERVES	**4**

1 Pour the hot water over the tomatoes in a small bowl. Let stand until the tomatoes are softened, about 10 minutes. Drain, then chop the tomatoes.

2 Heat the oil in a medium ovenproof skillet (such as cast iron) over medium-high heat. Add the onion, leek, and garlic; cook, stirring occasionally, until lightly browned, about 6 minutes. Add the chard and tomatoes; cook, stirring occasionally, until the chard is tender, about 3 minutes.

3 Meanwhile, preheat the broiler. Lightly beat the eggs, egg whites, salt, and pepper in a small bowl. Stir in the cheese.

4 Pour the egg mixture over the leek mixture, stirring gently to combine. Reduce the heat to medium. Cook, without stirring, until the eggs are set, about 7 minutes. Place skillet under the broiler about 4 inches from the heat and broil until the top of the frittata is lightly browned, about 2 minutes. Let stand 5 minutes before serving.

PER SERVING (¼ of frittata): 220 Cal, 10 g Fat, 2 g Sat Fat, 0 g Trans Fat, 218 mg Chol, 763 mg Sod, 14 g Carb, 3 g Fib, 19 g Prot, 334 mg Calc. **POINTS** value: **5.**

GOOD IDEA An unopened package of sun-dried tomatoes can be stored at room temperature up to 1 year. Once opened, store them in a zip-close plastic bag in a cool, dark place up to 6 months.

2 cups hot **water**

8 **sun-dried tomatoes** (not oil-packed)

4 teaspoons **extra-virgin olive oil**

1 **onion**, chopped

1 **leek**, trimmed to white part only, cleaned, and chopped

2 **garlic cloves**, minced

½ bunch **Swiss chard** (about ½ pound), tough stems removed, and leaves chopped

4 large **eggs**

2 **egg whites**

½ teaspoon **salt**

¼ teaspoon freshly **ground pepper**

1 cup shredded **fat-free mozzarella cheese**

Frittata with Sun-Dried
Tomatoes, Chard, and Leeks

Eggs with Bell Pepper and Onion

PREP	5 MINUTES
COOK	ABOUT 10 MINUTES
SERVES	4

1 Lightly beat the eggs, egg whites, and ¼ teaspoon of the salt in a medium bowl; set aside.

2 Heat the oil in a large nonstick skillet over medium-high heat. Add the onion, bell pepper, garlic, oregano, the remaining ¼ teaspoon salt, and the crushed red pepper; cook, stirring, until the onion begins to brown slightly and the vegetables are soft, about 5 minutes. Add the vinegar and cook 30 seconds.

3 Reduce the heat to medium; add the egg mixture and cook until almost set, about 1 minute. Continue cooking, lifting the edges frequently with a spatula to allow the uncooked egg to flow underneath, until the eggs are just set, about 3 minutes. Serve at once.

PER SERVING (about ¾ cup): 137 Cal, 9 g Fat, 2 g Sat Fat, 0 g Trans Fat, 212 mg Chol, 413 mg Sod, 4 g Carb, 1 g Fib, 10 g Prot, 36 mg Calc. **POINTS** value: **3.**

GOOD IDEA Serve this easy supper with toasted Italian bread and deduct it from your **weekly POINTS** Allowance (a 1-ounce chunk per serving will increase the **POINTS** value by 2).

4 large **eggs**

4 **egg whites**

½ teaspoon **salt**

1 tablespoon **extra-virgin olive oil**

1 small **onion,** thinly sliced

½ **green bell pepper,** thinly sliced

1 **garlic clove,** minced

½ teaspoon **dried oregano**

⅛ teaspoon **crushed red pepper**

1 teaspoon **sherry vinegar**

Vegetable Lasagna

PREP	20 MINUTES PLUS 20 MINUTES COOLING AND 10 MINUTES STANDING TIME
COOK	ABOUT 1 HOUR 10 MINUTES
SERVES	8

1 (8-ounce) package **whole-wheat lasagna noodles** (9 noodles), cooked and drained

8 teaspoons **extra-virgin olive oil**

1 **onion**, chopped

2 **garlic cloves**, minced

1 teaspoon **dried basil**

1 (28-ounce) **can crushed tomatoes**

¼ cup **tomato paste**

1 teaspoon **salt**

2 **zucchini**, halved lengthwise and thinly sliced

4 **carrots**, shredded

2 (15-ounce) containers **fat-free ricotta cheese**

2 cups shredded **fat-free mozzarella cheese**

1 large **egg**

1 Preheat the oven to 350°F. Spray a 9 x 13-inch baking dish with nonstick spray.

2 Heat 4 teaspoons of the oil in a large saucepan over medium-high heat. Add the onion, garlic, and basil; cook, stirring occasionally, until slightly softened, about 2 minutes. Stir in the tomatoes, tomato paste, and ½ teaspoon of the salt; bring to a boil. Reduce the heat and simmer, covered, until thickened, about 15 minutes. Remove from heat; cool sauce 10 minutes.

3 Heat the remaining 4 teaspoons oil in a large nonstick skillet over medium-high heat. Add the zucchini and cook, stirring occasionally, until lightly browned, about 6 minutes. Add the carrots and the remaining ½ teaspoon salt; cook, stirring occasionally, until the carrots soften, about 4 minutes. Remove the skillet from the heat; cool the vegetable mixture 10 minutes.

4 Combine the ricotta cheese, 1½ cups of the mozzarella cheese, and the egg, in a bowl.

5 Spread one-third of the sauce over the bottom of the baking pan. Top with 3 of the noodles. Spread half of the cheese mixture over the noodles. Top with half of the vegetables and one-third of the sauce. Repeat layering the 3 noodles, the remaining half of the cheese mixture, and the vegetables. Top with the remaining 3 noodles, one-third sauce, and ½ cup mozzarella cheese. Cover the lasagna with the foil and bake about 35 minutes. Uncover and bake until the lasagna is hot and bubbly, 10–12 minutes. Let stand 10 minutes before serving.

PER SERVING (⅛ of lasagna): 358 Cal, 7 g Fat, 1 g Sat Fat, 0 g Trans Fat, 49 mg Chol, 771 mg Sod, 47 g Carb, 8 g Fib, 27 g Prot, 485 mg Calc.
POINTS value: **7.**

Home-Style Lentils with Penne

PREP	ABOUT 25 MINUTES
COOK	NONE
SERVES	4

1 Heat the oil in a large saucepan over medium-high heat. Add the onion and garlic; cook, stirring occasionally, until slightly softened, about 2 minutes. Add the celery, carrots, and Italian seasoning; cook, stirring occasionally, until slightly softened, about 3 minutes. Stir in the water, lentils, and bay leaf; bring to a boil. Reduce the heat and gently boil, partially covered, until the lentils are tender but still hold their shape, 20–22 minutes. Discard bay leaf and stir in salt and pepper.

2 Meanwhile, cook the penne according to package directions. Divide the penne among 4 bowls; top each serving with the lentil mixture.

PER SERVING (¾ cup lentils and ¾ cup penne): 427 Cal, 6 g Fat, 1 g Sat Fat, 0 g Trans Fat, 0 mg Chol, 490 mg Sod, 77 g Carb, 18 g Fib, 22 g Prot, 89 mg Calc. *POINTS* value: *8.*

EXPRESS LANE Double the recipe for the lentils (Step 1) and freeze half for another meal to serve over brown rice or whole-wheat couscous.

4 teaspoons **extra-virgin olive oil**

1 **onion**, chopped

4 **garlic cloves**, minced

2 **celery** stalks, cut into ½-inch pieces

2 **carrots**, cut into ½-inch pieces

1 teaspoon **Italian seasoning**

3 cups **water**

1 cup **brown lentils**, picked over, rinsed, and drained

1 **bay leaf**

¾ teaspoon **salt**

¼ teaspoon freshly **ground pepper**

2 cups **whole-wheat penne**

Smoky Beans and Rice

PREP	**10 MINUTES**
COOK	**ABOUT 15 MINUTES**
SERVES	**6**

1 cup quick-cooking **brown rice**

4 teaspoons **extra-virgin olive oil**

1 **onion**, chopped

2 **garlic cloves**, minced

1 **red bell pepper**, seeded and chopped

1 teaspoon **ground coriander**

1 teaspoon **dried oregano**

¾ teaspoon **smoked paprika**

2 **plum tomatoes**, chopped

1 (15½-ounce) can **pinto beans**, drained (do not rinse)

1 (15½-ounce) can **black beans**, rinsed and drained

½ teaspoon **salt**

¼ teaspoon freshly **ground pepper**

1 Cook the rice according to package directions, omitting any fat.

2 Meanwhile, heat the oil in a large saucepan over medium-high heat. Add the onion and garlic; cook, stirring occasionally, until slightly softened, about 2 minutes. Add the bell pepper, coriander, oregano, and paprika; cook, stirring occasionally, until slightly softened, about 2 minutes. Add the tomatoes and cook, stirring occasionally, until slightly softened, about 2 minutes. Stir in the beans. Reduce the heat and simmer, covered, until vegetables are soft and the mixture is creamy, 8–10 minutes. Stir in the salt and pepper. Serve over the rice.

PER SERVING (⅔ cup bean mixture with ½ cup rice): 203 Cal, 4 g Fat, 0 g Sat Fat, 0 g Trans Fat, 0 mg Chol, 438 mg Sod, 36 g Carb, 7 g Fib, 7 g Prot, 57 mg Calc. **POINTS** value: **4.**

GOOD IDEA Smoked paprika can be found in large supermarkets and specialty food stores. If you can't find it, substitute ¼ teaspoon chipotle chili powder, but be aware, you'll be adding a touch of heat in the process.

Cuban Beans and Rice

PREP	10 MINUTES
COOK	ABOUT 45 MINUTES
SERVES	4

1 Cook the rice according to package directions, omitting any fat; keep warm.

2 Meanwhile, heat the oil in a large saucepan over medium-high heat. Add the garlic and pepper stir-fry; cook, stirring occasionally, until the vegetables soften and most of the liquid evaporates, 10–12 minutes. Add the tomatoes and cook, stirring occasionally, until slightly softened, about 2 minutes. Add the vinegar, cumin, fennel seeds, and pepper sauce; cook, stirring frequently, about 1 minute.

3 Stir in the beans; bring to a boil. Reduce the heat and simmer, covered, stirring occasionally, until the mixture slightly thickens and the vegetables are very tender, about 25 minutes. Serve with the rice.

PER SERVING (1 cup bean mixture and ½ cup rice): 252 Cal, 5 g Fat, 1 g Sat Fat, 0 g Trans Fat, 0 mg Chol, 538 mg Sod, 45 g Carb, 10 g Fib, 9 g Prot, 77 mg Calc. **POINTS** value: **5.**

½ cup **brown rice**

1 tablespoon **extra-virgin olive oil**

4 **garlic cloves**, minced

2 cups **frozen pepper stir-fry** (bell peppers and onion)

3 **plum tomatoes**, chopped

2 tablespoons **red-wine vinegar**

2 teaspoons **ground cumin**

1 teaspoon crushed **fennel seeds**

½ teaspoon **hot pepper sauce**

1 (15½-ounce) can **black beans**, drained (do not rinse)

1 (15½-ounce) can **pinto beans**, drained (do not rinse)

New Orleans Red Beans and Rice

PREP	10 MINUTES
COOK	ABOUT 10 MINUTES
SERVES	4

1 Prepare the rice according to package directions, omitting the fat; keep warm.

2 Heat the oil in a large nonstick skillet over medium-high heat. Add the celery, onion, bell pepper, garlic, chili powder, paprika, and cumin; cook, stirring frequently, until the vegetables start to soften, about 5 minutes. Add the tomatoes and bring to a boil. Reduce the heat and simmer, uncovered, until slightly thickened, about 4 minutes. Add the beans and simmer until heated through, about 2 minutes. Serve with the rice.

PER SERVING (scant ½ cup rice and 1 cup beans): 329 Cal, 7 g Fat, 1 g Sat Fat, 0 g Trans Fat, 0 mg Chol, 494 mg Sod, 55 g Carb, 11 g Fib, 11 g Prot, 84 mg Calc. *POINTS* value: *6.*

GOOD IDEA If you would like this dish a little more on the spicy side, serve it sprinkled with a few drops of hot pepper sauce.

¾ cup quick-cooking brown rice

1½ tablespoons extra-virgin olive oil

2 celery stalks, chopped

1 onion, chopped

1 green bell pepper, seeded and chopped

3 garlic cloves, minced

1 teaspoon chili powder

1 teaspoon paprika

½ teaspoon ground cumin

1 (14½-ounce) can diced tomatoes with basil, garlic, and oregano

1 (15½-ounce) can red kidney beans, rinsed and drained

Black Bean and
Avocado Tacos

Black Bean and Avocado Tacos

PREP	10 MINUTES
COOK	ABOUT 6 MINUTES
SERVES	6

1 tablespoon **extra-virgin olive oil**

1 **onion**, chopped

2 **garlic cloves**, minced

1 tablespoon reduced-sodium **taco seasoning**

1 (15½-ounce) can **black beans**, rinsed and drained

2 **plum tomatoes**, chopped

¼ cup **water**

6 **corn tortillas**

½ small **Haas avocado**, pitted, peeled, and diced

6 tablespoons prepared **pico de gallo**

4 tablespoons **light sour cream**

1 Heat the oil in a large nonstick skillet over high heat. Add the onion, garlic, and taco seasoning; cook, stirring occasionally, until the onion just starts to soften, about 2 minutes. Add the beans and cook, partially mashing with a wooden spoon, about 2 minutes. Stir in the tomatoes and water; cook until the tomatoes wilt and the water evaporates, about 2 minutes.

2 Meanwhile, warm the tortillas according to package directions. Top each tortilla with ⅓ cup of the bean mixture, ⅙ of the avocado, 1 tablespoon of the pico de gallo, and 2 teaspoons sour cream. Serve at once.

PER SERVING (1 taco): 202 Cal, 7 g Fat, 2 g Sat Fat, 0 g Trans Fat, 4 mg Chol, 363 mg Sod, 30 g Carb, 6 g Fib, 7 g Prot, 104 mg Calc. *POINTS* value: *4.*

DEFINITION Pico de gallo (PEE-koh day GI-yoh)—literally, "rooster's beak"—is a spicy Mexican relish that usually contains chopped jicama, oranges, onions, peppers, and chiles. Look for it in larger supermarkets or in Mexican groceries. If unavailable, substitute salsa.

Pasta e Fagioli

PREP	5 MINUTES
COOK	ABOUT 15 MINUTES
SERVES	6

1 Heat the oil in a large saucepan over high heat. Add the onion, celery, and garlic; cook, stirring occasionally, until the vegetables start to soften, about 2 minutes.

2 Add the broth, beans, tomatoes, and pasta; cover and bring to a boil over high heat. Uncover the saucepan and cook until the pasta is tender, about 10 minutes. Remove from the heat and stir in the parsley and pepper. Serve sprinkled with the cheese.

PER SERVING (generous 1 cup and 1 tablespoon cheese): 214 Cal, 3 g Fat, 0 g Sat Fat, 0 g Trans Fat, 0 mg Chol, 870 mg Sod, 39 g Carb, 6 g Fib, 9 g Prot, 87 mg Calc. *POINTS* value: *4.*

GOOD IDEA If you like, add another flavor layer by substituting ½ cup chopped fresh fennel bulb for the celery and adding ½ teaspoon of crushed fennel seeds with the onion, fennel, and garlic.

1 tablespoon **extra-virgin olive oil**

1 **onion**, chopped

2 **celery** stalks, chopped

4 **garlic cloves**, sliced

4 cups **vegetable broth**

1 (15½-ounce) can **cannellini** (white kidney) **beans**, rinsed and drained

1 (14½-ounce) can diced **tomatoes with basil, garlic,** and **oregano**

1 cup **alphabet-shape** or other **small pasta,** such as ditalini

3 tablespoons chopped **flat-leaf parsley**

¼ teaspoon freshly **ground pepper**

6 tablespoons **grated Asiago** or **Parmesan,** or **shredded sharp provolone cheese**

Vegetable Paella

PREP	15 MINUTES PLUS 5 MINUTES STANDING TIME
COOK	ABOUT 50 MINUTES
SERVES	4

1 Heat 2 teaspoons of the oil in a large nonstick skillet over medium-high heat. Add the onion and garlic; cook, stirring occasionally, until slightly softened, about 2 minutes. Stir in the celery, bell pepper, zucchini, and ½ teaspoon of the salt; cook, stirring occasionally, until the slightly softened, about 2 minutes. Transfer the vegetables to a bowl.

2 Heat the remaining 1 teaspoon oil in the same skillet over medium-high heat. Add the rice, saffron, and the remaining ¼ teaspoon salt; cook, stirring frequently, until rice is lightly toasted, about 1 minute. Stir in the broth. Reduce the heat and simmer, covered, until the rice is almost tender, about 30 minutes. Stir in the water; return the liquid to a simmer. Cook, covered, until the liquid is almost completely absorbed, about 10 minutes. Add the vegetables, beans, and peas; cook, covered, stirring occasionally, until heated through, about 5 minutes. Let the paella stand, covered, 5 minutes before serving.

PER SERVING (1¼ cups): 231 Cal, 5 g Fat, 1 g Sat Fat, 0 g Trans Fat, 0 mg Chol, 1,007 mg Sod, 41 g Carb, 7 g Fib, 8 g Prot, 69 mg Calc.
POINTS value: **4.**

3 teaspoons **extra-virgin olive oil**

1 **onion**, chopped

2 **garlic cloves**, minced

2 **celery** stalks, cut into ¾-inch pieces

1 **red bell pepper**, seeded cut into ¾-inch pieces

1 **zucchini**, quartered lengthwise and cut into ¾-inch pieces

¾ teaspoon **salt**

¾ cup quick-cooking **brown rice**

¼ teaspoon **saffron threads**, lightly crushed

1 (14½ounce) can **vegetable broth**

½ cup **water**

1 (15-ounce) can **cannellini (white kidney) beans**, rinsed and drained

½ cup **frozen peas**

Kasha and Chickpea Pilaf

PREP	15 MINUTES
COOK	ABOUT 20 MINUTES
SERVES	4

1 Heat 2 teaspoons of the oil in a large nonstick skillet over medium-high heat. Add the onion, zucchini, and bell pepper; cook, stirring occasionally, until the vegetables are tender and lightly golden, about 5 minutes. Add the chickpeas and cook, stirring frequently, about 1 minute. Transfer the vegetable mixture to a plate.

2 Meanwhile, bring the broth to a boil in a small saucepan.

3 Combine the kasha and egg in a medium bowl; mix well. Heat the remaining 2 teaspoons oil in the same skillet over medium-high heat. Add the kasha mixture and cook, stirring frequently, until the grains separate, about 1 minute. Stir in the boiling broth, the salt, and ground pepper. Reduce the heat and simmer, covered, until the liquid is absorbed and the kasha is tender, 8–10 minutes. Add the vegetable mixture and cook, stirring occasionally, until hot, about 1 minute.

PER SERVING (1½ cups): 293 Cal, 8 g Fat, 1 g Sat Fat, 0 g Trans Fat, 53 mg Chol, 884 mg Sod, 47 g Carb, 9 g Fib, 12 g Prot, 52 mg Calc. **POINTS** value: **6.**

DEFINITION Kasha (KAH-shuh) are roasted buckwheat groats. The trick to making tender, not mushy, kasha is to coat it with egg and stir it over moderately high heat until the grains separate. That also gives the grain a wonderful nutty flavor.

4 teaspoons **olive oil**

1 **onion**, chopped

1 medium **zucchini**, chopped

1 **red bell pepper**, seeded and chopped

1 cup canned **chickpeas**, rinsed and drained

2 cups **vegetable broth**

1 cup **kasha**

1 large **egg**, lightly beaten

¾ teaspoon **salt**

¼ teaspoon freshly **ground pepper**

Chickpea, Asparagus, and Corn Sauté

PREP	10 MINUTES
COOK	ABOUT 10 MINUTES
SERVES	4

1 Heat the oil in a large nonstick skillet over medium-high heat. Add the garlic and cook, stirring constantly, until fragrant, about 30 seconds. Add the corn and cook, stirring occasionally, until lightly browned, about 2 minutes. Add the asparagus and cook, stirring occasionally, until bright green, about 3 minutes. Add the chickpeas and cook, stirring occasionally, until the asparagus is tender, about 2 minutes.

2 Remove the skillet from the heat; stir in the tomatoes, onion, basil, salt, and pepper.

PER SERVING (1 cup): 171 Cal, 5 g Fat, 1 g Sat Fat, 0 g Trans Fat, 0 mg Chol, 435 mg Sod, 27 g Carb, 6 g Fib, 7 g Prot, 48 mg Calc. *POINTS* value: *3.*

GOOD IDEA Serve this dish right away or at room temperature with brown rice (½ cup for each serving will increase the *POINTS* value by 2).

1 tablespoon **extra-virgin olive oil**

3 **garlic cloves**, minced

1½ cups fresh or thawed frozen **corn kernels**

1 pound fresh **asparagus**, trimmed and cut into 1½-inch pieces

1 (1½-ounce) can **chickpeas**, rinsed and drained

1 cup **cherry tomatoes**, halved

½ small **red onion**, finely chopped

¼ cup thinly sliced **fresh basil**

½ teaspoon **salt**

¼ teaspoon freshly **ground pepper**

Minted Chickpeas and Carrots

PREP	15 MINUTES
COOK	NONE
SERVES	4

1 Combine the chickpeas, carrots, radishes, onion, and mint in a large bowl.

2 Combine the lemon juice, oil, garlic, cumin, salt, and pepper in a small bowl; toss with the chickpea mixture.

PER SERVING (about ¾ cup): 106 Cal, 3 g Fat, 0 g Sat Fat, 0 g Trans Fat, 0 mg Chol, 287 mg Sod, 16 g Carb, 5 g Fib, 4 g Prot, 50 mg Calc. *POINTS* value: *2.*

EXPRESS LANE Purchase a package of shredded carrots from the supermarket's produce section and this salad is practically prep-free.

1 (15½-ounce) can **chickpeas**, rinsed and drained

3 **carrots**, shredded

½ cup sliced **radishes**

¼ cup diced **red onion**

¼ cup chopped **fresh mint**

1 tablespoon **fresh lemon juice**

2 teaspoons **extra-virgin olive oil**

1 small **garlic clove**, crushed through a press

½ teaspoon **ground cumin**

¼ teaspoon **salt**

⅛ teaspoon freshly **ground pepper**

Bulgur Pilaf with Roasted Tomatoes, Chickpeas, and Spinach

PREP	15 MINUTES
COOK	ABOUT 55 MINUTES
SERVES	6

1 Preheat the oven to 400°F. Spray a large baking pan with olive oil nonstick spray.

2 Combine the tomatoes, onion, garlic, and oil in a large bowl; toss to coat. Arrange the tomato mixture in a single layer on the baking pan. Roast, stirring once, 30 minutes. Stir in the chickpeas; roast until vegetables are evenly browned, about 15 minutes. Remove the pan from the oven. Add 1 cup of the broth, stirring to scrape the brown bits from the bottom of the pan.

3 Transfer roasted vegetable mixture to a large saucepan. Stir in the remaining 1½ cups broth, the salt, and pepper; bring to a boil. Stir in the bulgur. Reduce the heat and simmer, covered, until the bulgur is tender and the liquid is absorbed, about 10 minutes. Remove the garlic; stir in the spinach until wilted.

PER SERVING (1 cup): 259 Cal, 4 g Fat, 1 g Sat Fat, 0 g Trans Fat, 0 mg Chol, 629 mg Sod, 50 g Carb, 12 g Fib, 10 g Prot, 49 mg Calc.
POINTS value: **5.**

GOOD IDEA Top each serving with ¼ cup plain fat-free yogurt and increase the per-serving **POINTS** value by ½.

1 pound **plum tomatoes**, quartered

1 large **red onion**, cut into ½-inch-thick slices

4 **garlic cloves**, crushed

1 tablespoon **olive oil**

1 (15½-ounce) can **chickpeas**, rinsed and drained

2½ cups **vegetable broth**

¼ teaspoon **salt**

⅛ teaspoon freshly **ground pepper**

2 cups **bulgur**

2 cups firmly packed **fresh baby spinach**

Aromatic Vegetable Couscous

PREP	5 MINUTES PLUS 5 MINUTES STANDING TIME
COOK	ABOUT 10 MINUTES
SERVES	4

1 Bring the orange juice, water, and ½ teaspoon of the salt to a boil in a small saucepan. Add the couscous, cover, and remove from the heat. Let stand 5 minutes, then fluff the couscous with a fork.

2 Meanwhile, heat the oil in a large nonstick skillet over high heat. Add the zucchini, yellow squash, onion, garlic, curry powder, cinnamon, cayenne, and the remaining ¼ teaspoon salt. Cook, stirring frequently, until the vegetables start to soften, about 5 minutes. Add the chickpeas and tomatoes; bring to a boil. Reduce the heat and simmer, stirring occasionally, until slightly thickened, about 5 minutes. Serve over the couscous.

PER SERVING (¾ cup couscous and 1¼ cups vegetable mixture): 366 Cal, 7 g Fat, 1 g Sat Fat, 0 g Trans Fat, 0 mg Chol, 708 mg Sod, 67 g Carb, 11 g Fib, 16 g Prot, 128 mg Calc. *POINTS* value: *7.*

GOOD IDEA For extra flavor, garnish with thin strips of orange zest.

¾ cup **orange juice**

½ cup **water**

¾ teaspoon **salt**

1 cup **whole-wheat couscous**

1 tablespoon **extra-virgin olive oil**

1 medium (8-ounce) **zucchini**, cut into ¼-inch slices

1 medium (8-ounce) **yellow squash**, cut into ¼-inch slices

1 **onion**, chopped

3 **garlic cloves**, sliced

1 teaspoon **curry powder**

½ teaspoon **cinnamon**

⅛ teaspoon **cayenne**

1 (15½-ounce) can **chickpeas**, rinsed sand drained

1 (14½-ounce) **can diced tomatoes**

Aromatic Vegetable
Couscous

Asian Noodles with Peanut Dressing

PREP	5 MINUTES
COOK	ABOUT 10 MINUTES
SERVES	4

6 ounces **lo mein noodles**

1 (12-ounce) **bag pre-cut vegetables for stir-fry** (try broccoli, carrots, and snow peas)

⅓ cup **reduced-fat peanut butter**

3 tablespoons **water**

3 tablespoons packed **light brown sugar**

1 tablespoon **seasoned rice vinegar**

1 tablespoon reduced-sodium **soy sauce**

1 tablespoon **hoisin sauce**

1 tablespoon **tomato paste**

1 teaspoon **Asian (dark) sesame oil**

1 Cook the noodles according to package directions, adding the stir-fry vegetables during the last 3 minutes of cooking time. Drain and keep warm.

2 Meanwhile, whisk together the peanut butter, water, sugar, vinegar, soy sauce, hoisin sauce, tomato paste, and sesame oil in a serving bowl until smooth. Add the noodles and vegetables; toss well to coat. Serve at once while hot or let come to room temperature before serving.

PER SERVING (1 cup): 383 Cal, 10 g Fat, 2 g Sat Fat, 0 g Trans Fat, 0 mg Chol, 737 mg Sod, 61 g Carb, 6 g Fib, 15 g Prot, 52 mg Calc. **POINTS** value: **8.**

FOOD NOTE Pack up any leftovers and refrigerate for up to 3 days. Reheat with a little water or simply, let them come to room temperature before serving.

Moo Shu Veggie Fajitas

PREP	10 MINUTES
COOK	ABOUT 10 MINUTES
SERVES	4

1 tablespoon **Asian (dark) sesame oil**

1 **onion**, thinly sliced

1 (3–4-ounce) package sliced **fresh shiitake mushrooms**

1 tablespoon grated **fresh ginger**

2 **garlic cloves**, minced

½ small head **napa cabbage**, shredded

1 cup shredded **carrots**

3 tablespoons **hoisin sauce**

4 (8-inch) **fat-free flour tortillas**

4 teaspoons **light sour cream**

1 Heat a large nonstick skillet or wok over high heat until a drop of water sizzles. Pour in the oil and swirl to coat the pan. Add the onion, mushrooms, ginger, and garlic; stir-fry until softened, about 5 minutes. Add the cabbage and carrots; stir-fry until the carrots are crisp-tender, about 3 minutes. Stir in the hoisin sauce and cook 30 seconds more.

2 Meanwhile, warm the tortillas according to package directions. Top each with ½ cup of the vegetable mixture and 1 teaspoon of the sour cream; roll up and serve at once.

PER SERVING (1 fajita): 259 Cal, 5 g Fat, 1 g Sat Fat, 0 g Trans Fat, 2 mg Chol, 679 mg Sod, 46 g Carb, 4 g Fib, 8 g Prot, 147 mg Calc.
POINTS value: **5.**

FOOD NOTE If you prefer, serve the stir-fried vegetables over brown rice rather than rolling them in tortillas and boost the protein with some sautéed cubed tofu or soy protein crumbles.

Barley Vegetable Soup

Barley Vegetable Soup

PREP	10 MINUTES
COOK	ABOUT 12 MINUTES
SERVES	6

1 Bring the water to a boil in a medium saucepan over high heat. Add the barley. Reduce the heat and simmer, covered, until tender, about 10 minutes. Remove the pan from the heat and set aside.

2 Meanwhile, heat the oil in a large saucepan over high heat. Add the onions, mushrooms, carrots, celery, garlic, and oregano. Cook, stirring occasionally, until the vegetables are softened, about 5 minutes. Add the broth, tomato paste, and parsley; bring to a boil. Reduce the heat and simmer, covered, until the vegetables are tender, about 5 minutes. Stir in the barley and heat through, about 1 minute.

PER SERVING (¾ cup): 206 Cal, 5 g Fat, 1 g Sat Fat, 0 g Trans Fat, 0 mg Chol, 757 mg Sod, 37 g Carb, 8 g Fib, 5 g Prot, 49 mg Calc.
POINTS value: **4.**

EXPRESS LANE Plan ahead for an extra meal by doubling this recipe. Refrigerate half for up to 3 days, or freeze it for up to 6 months.

2 cups **water**

1 cup quick-cooking **barley**

2 tablespoons **extra-virgin olive oil**

2 **onions**, chopped

2 cups sliced **fresh white mushrooms** (about 5 ounces)

2 **carrots**, chopped

2 **celery stalks**, chopped

3 **garlic cloves**, minced

2 teaspoons **dried oregano**

4 cups **vegetable broth**

3 tablespoons **tomato paste**

3 **fresh parsley sprigs**

CHAPTER 8

Savory Sides

Roast Asparagus and Plum Tomatoes

PREP	10 MINUTES
COOK	ABOUT 15 MINUTES
SERVES	4

1 pound fresh **asparagus**, trimmed and cut into 4-inch lengths

1½ pounds **plum tomatoes**, halved lengthwise

2½ teaspoons **extra-virgin olive oil**

1½ teaspoons **white-wine vinegar**

1 small **garlic clove**, minced

½ teaspoon grated **lemon zest**

¼ teaspoon **salt**

⅛ teaspoon freshly **ground pepper**

1 Arrange the oven rack in the lower third of the oven. Preheat the oven to 425°F.

2 Toss the asparagus and tomatoes with 1 teaspoon of the oil in a roasting pan. Arrange the vegetables in a single layer, with the tomatoes cut-side up. Roast until the tomatoes are lightly charred and the asparagus are just tender, 12–16 minutes, depending on the thickness of the asparagus.

3 Meanwhile, combine the remaining 1½ teaspoons oil, the vinegar, garlic, lemon zest, salt, and pepper in a cup. Transfer the vegetables to a platter and drizzle with the dressing.

PER SERVING (about 1 cup): 78 Cal, 4 g Fat, 1 g Sat Fat, 0 g Trans Fat, 0 mg Chol, 163 mg Sod, 11 g Carb, 3 g Fib, 3 g Prot, 23 mg Calc. **POINTS** value: **1.**

HOW WE DID IT Thin asparagus do not need to be peeled. Just cut off and discard the tough lighter-colored part at the ends, and roast the stalks for the least amount of time specified. If your asparagus spears are thick, simply peel the lower part of the stalks with a vegetable peeler.

Roast Asparagus and
Plum Tomatoes

Miso-Glazed Asparagus

PREP	10 MINUTES
COOK	ABOUT 20 MINUTES
SERVES	6

2 pounds fresh **asparagus**, trimmed

¼ teaspoon freshly **ground pepper**

1 tablespoon **light miso paste**

1 tablespoon fresh **lime juice**

1 Preheat the oven to 450°F. Spray a large jelly-roll pan with canola nonstick spray. Arrange the asparagus in a single layer in the pan; spray with canola nonstick spray and sprinkle with the pepper. Roast the asparagus, shaking the pan occasionally, until crisp-tender, about 15 minutes.

2 Meanwhile, combine the miso and lime juice in a small bowl. Remove the pan from the oven; toss the asparagus with the miso mixture. Bake the asparagus until tender and glazed, about 3 minutes.

PER SERVING (about 6 asparagus spears): 28 Cal, 1 g Fat, 0 g Sat Fat, 0 g Trans Fat, 0 mg Chol, 228 mg Sod, 4 g Carb, 1 g Fib, 2 g Prot, 15 mg Calc. **POINTS** value: **0**.

DEFINITION Miso (MEE-soh) is fermented soybean paste, a mainstay in Japanese cooking. Light miso, which is golden in color, is traditionally used in delicate soups and sauces—but we've discovered it's wonderful with vegetables too. Look for miso in Asian markets, large supermarkets, or natural-foods stores.

Microwave Broccoli with Spicy Garlic Oil

PREP	10 MINUTES
COOK	ABOUT 5 MINUTES
SERVES	4

1 Combine the broccoli and water in a large microwavable bowl. Cover with plastic wrap, then prick a few holes in the plastic. Microwave on High until the broccoli is crisp-tender, 3–3½ minutes, stirring once halfway through cooking. Drain. Return the broccoli to the same bowl and set aside.

2 Combine the oil, garlic, and crushed red pepper in a small microwavable bowl. Microwave on High until the garlic sizzles, 30–45 seconds. Add the oil mixture and salt to the broccoli; toss to coat. Serve with the lemon wedges.

PER SERVING (about 1¼ cups): 77 Cal, 5 g Fat, 1 g Sat Fat, 0 g Trans Fat, 0 mg Chol, 177 mg Sod, 8 g Carb, 4 g Fib, 4 g Prot, 61 mg Calc.
POINTS value: *1.*

GOOD IDEA Stir 2⅔ cups hot cooked whole-wheat penne into the broccoli mixture and you've got a great pasta main dish (⅔ cup cooked whole-wheat pasta for each serving will increase the **POINTS** value by 2).

1 pound fresh **broccoli crowns, cut into florets**

2 tablespoons **water**

4 teaspoons **extra-virgin olive oil**

1 large **garlic clove,** minced

¼ teaspoon **crushed red pepper**

¼ teaspoon **salt**

4 **lemon** wedges

Grilled Corn in the Husk

PREP	10 MINUTES
COOK	6–8 MINUTES
SERVES	6

6 **corn-on-the-cob**
(husks still on)

1 Preheat the grill.

2 Pull off and discard all but the innermost layer of husk from each ear of corn (you should be able to see the kernels through the barely translucent husk). Cut off the tassel of corn silks at the end of each ear, using kitchen scissors (don't bother removing the silk strands underneath the husk as they will disintegrate as the corn cooks).

3 Grill the corn, turning every 2 minutes, until black grill marks appear all over the husks, and the corn silks are blackened, 6–8 minutes.

4 To serve, pull back the corn husks, and brush away the burned corn silk strands. (Or, if you prefer, simply remove the husks completely and serve.)

PER SERVING (1 corn-on-the-cob): 133 Cal, 2 g Fat, 0 g Sat Fat, 0 g Trans Fat, 0 mg Chol, 21 mg Sod, 31 g Carb, 3 g Fib, 4 g Prot, 2 mg Calc. **POINTS** value: **2.**

ZAP IT Corn-on-the-cob is now more readily available year-round, and, if you have a hankering for some, it's a snap to prepare in the microwave. Arrange no more than 4 corn-on-the-cob, each wrapped in damp paper towels, in the microwave. Microwave on High until hot, about 2 minutes for each ear.

Cauliflower-Leek Bake

PREP	10 MINUTES
COOK	ABOUT 25 MINUTES
SERVES	4

1 tablespoon **olive oil**

4 cups fresh **cauliflower florets**

1 cup thinly sliced **leeks**

¼ cup **water**

¼ teaspoon **salt**

⅛ teaspoon freshly **ground pepper**

1 Preheat the oven to 450°F. Pour the oil into a shallow 2-quart baking dish; heat the dish in the oven 2 minutes. Add the cauliflower to the dish, toss to coat with the oil. Cover the dish with foil. Bake 15 minutes.

2 Remove the dish from the oven; stir in the leeks, water, salt, and pepper. Bake, covered, until the cauliflower is tender, 5–7 minutes.

PER SERVING (1 cup): 66 Cal, 4 g Fat, 1 g Sat Fat, 0 g Trans Fat, 0 mg Chol, 164 mg Sod, 7 g Carb, 3 g Fib, 2 g Prot, 29 mg Calc. **POINTS** value: *1.*

EXPRESS LANE Save time by purchasing a package of cauliflower florets from the produce section at the supermarket (or you can use broccoli florets).

Fried Green Plantains

Fried Green Plantains

PREP	5 MINUTES
COOK	ABOUT 12 MINUTES
SERVES	4

4 teaspoons **olive oil**

2 (10-ounce) **green plantains**, peeled and sliced on the diagonal ½-inch thick

1 **garlic clove**

¼ teaspoon **salt**

1 Heat the oil in a large nonstick skillet over medium-high heat. Add the plantains and cook until tender and golden brown, about 5 minutes on each side. Remove and spread out between several layers of paper towels. With the bottom of a heavy plate or skillet, gently press down on the slices, one at a time, to flatten them to half their thickness. Rub them gently with the garlic.

2 Spray the same skillet with olive oil nonstick spray and set over medium-high heat. Add the pressed slices and cook until heated through, about 1 minute on each side. Sprinkle with the salt. Serve at once.

PER SERVING (½ cup, about 5 pieces): 185 Cal, 3 g Fat, 0 Sat Fat, 0 g Trans Fat, 0 Chol, 153 mg Sod, 44 g Carb, 3 g Fiber, 1 g Prot, 4 mg Calc. **POINTS** value: **3.**

HOW WE DID IT A plantain looks like it should be as simple to peel as a banana—but the thick skin doesn't slip off quite so easily. To peel a plantain, cut off its ends, then cut it in half crosswise. Slit the skin along its ridges, cutting down to the flesh, and peel back the skin in strips.

Roasted Radishes and Carrots

PREP	10 MINUTES
COOK	ABOUT 25 MINUTES
SERVES	4

1 Preheat the oven to 425°F. Spray a small roasting pan with olive oil nonstick spray. Put the radishes and carrots in the pan; toss with the oil, thyme, salt, and pepper. Spread the vegetables into a single layer.

2 Roast the radishes and carrots, stirring once, until the vegetables are golden and tender, about 25 minutes. Stir in the chives and vinegar.

PER SERVING (¾ cup): 85 Cal, 3 g Fat, 0 g Sat Fat, 0 g Trans Fat, 0 mg Chol, 191 mg Sod, 14 g Carb, 2 g Fib, 2 g Prot, 56 mg Calc.
POINTS value: **2.**

2 bunches **radishes** (about 1 pound), trimmed and cut in half

1 (1-pound) bag **baby carrots**, cut in half lengthwise

2 teaspoons **olive oil**

1 teaspoon chopped **fresh thyme**

¼ teaspoon **kosher salt**

¼ teaspoon freshly **ground pepper**

2 tablespoons chopped **fresh chives**

1½ teaspoons **balsamic vinegar**

Mexican Squash Stew

PREP	20 MINUTES
COOK	ABOUT 25 MINUTES
SERVES	4

1 Heat the oil in a large nonstick skillet over medium-high heat. Add the onion and the bell and poblano peppers (if using canned chiles, add them with the squash in Step 2); cook, stirring occasionally, until softened, about 8 minutes. Stir in the garlic, oregano, chili powder, and cumin; cook, stirring constantly, about 1 minute.

2 Stir in the squash, broth, and canned chiles, if using; bring to a simmer. Reduce the heat and cook, stirring occasionally, until the squash is just soft enough to pierce with a fork, about 15 minutes. Sprinkle with the lime juice and cilantro just before serving.

PER SERVING (1½ cups): 138 Cal, 3 g Fat, 0 g Sat Fat, 0 g Trans Fat, 0 mg Chol, 243 mg Sod, 30 g Carb, 6 g Fib, 3 g Prot, 90 mg Calc.
POINTS value: *2.*

ZAP IT This stew makes great leftovers, and its flavor actually improves with time—just cover and refrigerate up to 3 days. Reheat it in the microwave, which will preserve the squash's texture better than stovetop cooking.

2 teaspoons **vegetable oil**

1 **onion**, chopped

1 **green bell pepper**, seeded and chopped

1 **poblano pepper**, seeded and chopped (wear gloves to prevent irritation) or 1 (4-ounce) can chopped **green chiles**, drained

2 **garlic cloves**, minced

1 teaspoon **dried oregano**

1 teaspoon **chili powder**

½ teaspoon **ground cumin**

1 (1½-pound) **butternut squash**, peeled and cut into ½-inch cubes

2 (14½-ounce) cans reduced-sodium **vegetable broth**

Juice of 1 lime (about ¼ cup)

3 tablespoons minced **fresh cilantro**

Microwave Ratatouille

PREP	20 MINUTES
COOK	ABOUT 20 MINUTES
SERVES	6

1 Combine the eggplant and 4 teaspoons of the oil in a large microwavable bowl. Cover with plastic wrap, then prick a few holes in the plastic. Microwave on High until the eggplant is softened, 4–4½ minutes.

2 Add the zucchini, tomatoes, bell peppers, fennel, onion, tomato paste, garlic, salt, pepper, and the remaining 2 teaspoons oil; toss well. Microwave, covered, until the vegetables are tender, 15 minutes, stirring every 5 minutes. Stir in the basil. Serve warm or at room temperature.

PER SERVING (generous ¾ cup): 119 Cal, 5 g Fat, 1 g Sat Fat, 0 g Trans Fat, 0 mg Chol, 405 mg Sod, 18 g Carb, 6 g Fib, 4 g Prot, 55 mg Calc. *POINTS* value: *2.*

GOOD IDEA For an extra boost of flavor, add 12 large brine-cured olives, such as Gaeta olives, pitted and coarsely chopped, in Step 2 with the basil (3 large olives for each serving will increase the *POINTS* value by ½).

1 medium **eggplant**, diced

6 teaspoons **extra-virgin olive oil**

2 medium **zucchini**, diced

1 (14½-ounce) can diced **tomatoes**, drained

1 **red bell pepper**, seeded and diced

1 **yellow bell pepper**, seeded and diced

1 small **fennel bulb**, diced

1 **onion**, diced

3 tablespoons **tomato paste**

1 large **garlic clove**, minced

¾ teaspoon **salt**

¼ teaspoon freshly **ground pepper**

2 tablespoons chopped **fresh basil**

Microwave Ratatouille

Roasted Root Vegetables

PREP	15 MINUTES
COOK	ABOUT 55 MINUTES
SERVES	4

1 pound **carrots**, halved lengthwise and cut into 2-inch lengths

1 pound **all-purpose potatoes**, cut into 2-inch chunks

2 **onions**, cut into eighths

4 teaspoons **olive oil**

2 sprigs **fresh thyme** or rosemary, or 2 teaspoons dried

¼ teaspoon **salt**

4–6 **garlic cloves** (optional)

Freshly **ground pepper**, to taste

1 Arrange the oven rack in the top third of the oven; preheat the oven to 400°F. Spray a large, shallow roasting pan or heavy jelly-roll pan with olive oil nonstick spray.

2 Bring the carrots and enough cold water to cover to a boil in a large saucepan or Dutch oven. Reduce the heat and simmer, covered, until the carrots are tender enough to nearly pierce through with a fork but are still quite firm, about 8 minutes. Drain.

3 Put the carrots, potatoes, and onions in the roasting pan. Drizzle with the oil and sprinkle with the thyme and salt; toss to evenly coat. Spread the vegetables in a single layer.

4 Roast 20 minutes, turning the vegetables and shaking the pan after 10 minutes. Stir in the garlic, if using. Roast until the vegetables are evenly browned and tender, 15–20 minutes longer, removing any fully cooked vegetables sooner, if necessary. Sprinkle with pepper.

PER SERVING (1 cup): 200 Cal, 5 g Fat, 1 g Sat Fat, 0 g Trans Fat, 0 mg Chol, 215 mg Sod, 36 g Carb, 6 g Fib, 5 g Prot, 62 mg Calc. **POINTS** value: **4.**

HOW WE DID IT In order for the vegetables to roast properly, be sure not to crowd them in the roasting pan. If the pan is too small, prepare a second pan to accommodate the excess, or roast the vegetables in 2 batches.

Spring Vegetable Sauté

PREP	10 MINUTES
COOK	ABOUT 10 MINUTES
SERVES	6

1 Heat the oil a large nonstick skillet over medium-high heat. Add the scallions and asparagus; cook, stirring occasionally, until crisp-tender, about 5 minutes.

2 Stir in the watercress, lemon juice, salt, and pepper. Cook, stirring occasionally, until the watercress just starts to wilt, about 2 minutes. Serve at once. Or cover and refrigerate up to 2 days and serve chilled.

PER SERVING (½ cup): 29 Cal, 2 g Fat, 0 g Sat Fat, 0 g Trans Fat, 0 mg Chol, 213 mg Sod, 3 g Carb, 1 g Fib, 2 g Prot, 55 mg Calc. **POINTS** value: *1*.

GOOD IDEA Garnish the dish with thin strips of lemon zest. Or sprinkle 2 tablespoons freshly grated Parmesan cheese on each serving (remember to deduct it from your weekly **POINTS** Allowance—2 tablespoons will increase the **POINTS** value by 1).

2 teaspoons **olive oil**

1 bunch **scallions**, sliced on the diagonal (whites and 2 inches of green part only)

1 bunch fresh **asparagus**, trimmed and cut into diagonal 1-inch pieces

1 bunch **watercress**, cleaned and coarsely chopped

2 teaspoons fresh **lemon juice**

½ teaspoon **salt**

Freshly **ground pepper**, to taste

Grilled Vegetables
with Salsa Fresca

Grilled Vegetables with Salsa Fresca

☑ ✨

PREP	15 MINUTES PLUS 15 MINUTES STANDING TIME
COOK	ABOUT 10 MINUTES
SERVES	4

1 To make the salsa, combine the tomatoes, onion, cilantro, lemon juice, ¼ teaspoon of the salt, the cumin, and cayenne in a food processor; pulse until coarsely chopped. Transfer the salsa to a small bowl. Let stand until the flavors develop, about 15 minutes.

2 Meanwhile, spray the grill rack with olive oil nonstick spray; prepare the grill.

3 Lightly spray the eggplants, zucchini, and squash with olive oil nonstick spray. Place the vegetables on the grill rack. Sprinkle with the remaining ½ teaspoon salt. Grill, turning occasionally, until the vegetables are lightly charred and softened, about 10 minutes. Serve with the salsa.

PER SERVING (¼ of vegetables with 3 tablespoons salsa): 87 Cal, 1 g Fat, 0 g Sat Fat, 0 g Trans Fat, 0 mg Chol, 445 mg Sod, 19 g Carb, 7 g Fib, 4 g Prot, 39 mg Calc. **POINTS** value: **1**.

EXPRESS LANE If you want, prepare the salsa ahead and refrigerate in an airtight container up to 3 days.

1 cup **grape tomatoes**

½ small **red onion**

2 tablespoons fresh **cilantro leaves**

2 teaspoons fresh **lemon juice**

¾ teaspoon **salt**

¼ teaspoon **ground cumin**

⅛ teaspoon **cayenne**

3 Italian **baby eggplants**, each cut into 4 lengthwise slices

2 medium **zucchini**, each cut into 4 lengthwise slices

1 **yellow squash**, cut into 4 lengthwise slices

Mashed Potatoes Gremolata

PREP	15 MINUTES
COOK	ABOUT 30 MINUTES
SERVES	6

1 Combine the potatoes and enough cold water to cover by 2 inches in a large saucepan; bring to a boil. Reduce the heat and simmer, covered, until the potatoes are fork-tender, 15–18 minutes.

2 Drain the potatoes in a colander. Heat the oil in the same saucepan over low heat. Add the garlic and cook, stirring constantly, until fragrant, about 30 seconds. Add the potatoes and cook, stirring frequently, until dry, about 2 minutes.

3 Meanwhile, microwave the broth on High in a glass measure until hot, about 1 minute.

4 Coarsely mash the potatoes with a potato masher or wooden spoon; stir in the hot broth, the parsley, lemon zest, salt, and pepper until blended.

PER SERVING (½ cup): 145 Cal, 2 g Fat, 0 g Sat Fat, 0 g Trans Fat, 0 mg Chol, 704 mg Sod, 30 g Carb, 3 g Fib, 3 g Prot, 16 mg Calc.
POINTS value: **2.**

ZAP IT These spuds are best served immediately, but you can let them stand at room temperature up to 1 hour and reheat them in the microwave. Just transfer the potatoes to a microwavable bowl; cover and microwave on High until heated through, 1 to 2 minutes.

2 pounds **red potatoes**, peeled and quartered

2 teaspoons **extra-virgin olive oil**

1 large **garlic clove**, minced

½ cup reduced-sodium **chicken broth**

2 tablespoons chopped **fresh parsley**

¾ teaspoon grated **lemon zest**

¾ teaspoon **salt**

¼ teaspoon freshly **ground pepper**

Twice-Baked Potatoes

PREP	10 MINUTES PLUS 30 MINUTES COOLING TIME
COOK	ABOUT 1 HOUR 10 MINUTES
SERVES	6

3 (½-pound) **baking potatoes**, scrubbed

1 tablespoon **olive oil**

½ cup shredded **fat-free cheddar cheese**

⅓ cup **fat-free buttermilk**

¼ cup **fat-free sour cream**

3 tablespoons minced **fresh chives**

Freshly **ground pepper**, to taste

1 Preheat the oven to 400°F. Line a baking sheet with foil. Prick the potatoes in several places with a fork; place on the baking sheet. Bake until fork-tender, about 1 hour. Transfer to a rack to cool about 30 minutes (leave the oven on).

2 Cut each potato lengthwise in half. Scoop out the flesh from each half, leaving a ¼-inch-thick layer still in the shell. Transfer the potato flesh to a medium bowl. Return the potato shells to the oven to crisp as you prepare the filling.

3 Mash the potato flesh and oil with a fork until smooth. Stir in the cheese, buttermilk, sour cream, chives, and pepper.

4 Remove the potato shells from the oven; increase the heat to 500°F. Using an oven mitt to protect your hand, stuff each potato half with a mound of the filling. Bake until browned on top, about 10 minutes. Serve at once.

PER SERVING (1 filled potato half): 133 Cal, 3 g Fat, 0 g Sat Fat, 0 g Trans Fat, 4 mg Chol, 130 mg Sod, 22 g Carb, 2 g Fib, 7 g Prot, 134 mg Calc. **POINTS** value: **3.**

HOW WE DID IT While preparing the filling in Step 3, leave the potato shells in the oven to crisp at least 5 minutes but no more than 10 minutes or they may become tough.

Baked Sweet Potatoes with Mango Raita

PREP	10 MINUTES
COOK	ABOUT 45 MINUTES
SERVES	4

1 Preheat the oven to 400°F. Prick the potatoes in several places with a fork. Place the potatoes on the oven rack and bake until fork-tender, about 45 minutes.

2 Meanwhile, combine the mango, yogurt, cilantro, salt, and cayenne in a bowl.

3 Cut each potato lengthwise in half; top each half with mango raita.

PER SERVING (1 potato with $\frac{1}{2}$ cup raita): 219 Cal, 0 g Fat, 0 g Sat Fat, 0 g Trans Fat, 0 mg Chol, 196 mg Sod, 51 g Carb, 6 g Fib, 6 g Prot, 125 mg Calc. **POINTS** value: **4.**

ZAP IT To cut the cooking time, you can microwave the sweet potatoes. Prick the potatoes with a fork; arrange 1-inch apart in the microwave. Microwave on High, rearranging once, until almost tender, about 10 minutes. Let the potatoes stand 5 minutes, then proceed with the recipe as directed.

4 small **sweet potatoes** (2$\frac{1}{4}$ pounds), scrubbed

1 large ripe **mango**, peeled and finely chopped

1 cup plain **fat-free yogurt**

$\frac{1}{4}$ cup **fresh cilantro** leaves

$\frac{1}{4}$ teaspoon **salt**

$\frac{1}{8}$ teaspoon **cayenne**

Baked Sweet Potatoes
with Mango Raita

Curried Sweet Potato Wedges

PREP	10 MINUTES
COOK	ABOUT 35–40 MINUTES
SERVES	6

2 pounds **sweet potatoes**, scrubbed

1 tablespoon **canola oil**

2 teaspoons **curry powder**

½ teaspoon **salt**

Pinch **cayenne**

1 Preheat the oven to 450°F. Halve the potatoes and cut each piece lengthwise into quarters. Toss with the oil, curry powder, salt, and cayenne in a large bowl.

2 Arrange the potatoes in a single layer on a large nonstick baking sheet. Bake, turning once, until browned and crisp, 35–40 minutes.

PER SERVING (⅔ cup): 169 Cal, 3 g Fat, 0 g Sat Fat, 0 g Trans Fat, 0 mg Chol, 209 mg Sod, 35 g Carb, 5 g Fib, 3 g Prot, 38 mg Calc. **POINTS** value: **3.**

GOOD IDEA Here's a tasty dip to serve with the wedges: Combine 1 cup plain fat-free yogurt, 2 tablespoons chopped fresh cilantro, 2 tablespoons chopped scallions, and ¼ teaspoon salt in a medium bowl (¼ cup dip for each serving will increase the **POINTS** value by ½).

Microwave Brown Rice and Shiitake Pilaf

PREP	5 MINUTES
COOK	ABOUT 15 MINUTES
SERVES	4

1 Microwave the rice according to package directions; set aside and keep warm.

2 Combine the bell pepper, shallot, and oil in a 3-quart microwavable casserole with a lid. Cover and microwave on High until the bell pepper softens, 1½–2 minutes. Stir in the mushrooms and microwave, covered, until tender, 1½–2 minutes. Stir in the rice, lemon zest, salt, and pepper.

PER SERVING (about 1 cup): 167 Cal, 3 g Fat, 0 g Sat Fat, 0 g Trans Fat, 0 mg Chol, 304 mg Sod, 30 g Carb, 3 g Fib, 4 g Prot, 21 mg Calc.
POINTS value: **3.**

GOOD IDEA For a pleasant crunch, garnish this easy pilaf with 2 tablespoons sliced toasted almonds and deduct it from your **weekly POINTS** Allowance (½ tablespoon for each serving will increase the **POINTS** value by ½).

1 cup quick-cooking **brown rice**

1 **red bell pepper**, seeded and diced

1 large **shallot**, finely chopped

2 teaspoons **olive oil**

½ pound **fresh shiitake mushrooms**, stems discarded and sliced

½ teaspoon grated **lemon zest**

½ teaspoon **salt**

⅛ teaspoon freshly **ground pepper**

Tropical Couscous

Tropical Couscous

PREP	10 MINUTES PLUS 5 MINUTES STANDING TIME
COOK	5 MINUTES
SERVES	6

1 Bring the water to a boil in a small saucepan. Add the couscous, oil, salt, and ground pepper, stirring to remove any lumps. Remove the saucepan from the heat, cover, and let the couscous stand 5 minutes.

2 Using 2 forks, gently fluff the couscous, taking care to break up the lumps. Transfer the couscous to a large bowl; stir in the mango, bell pepper, scallions, cilantro, vinegar, and orange zest.

PER SERVING (⅔ cup): 180 Cal, 2 g Fat, 0 g Sat Fat, 0 g Trans Fat, 0 mg Chol, 292 mg Sod, 37 g Carb, 6 g Fib, 6 g Prot, 21 mg Calc.
POINTS value: **3.**

HOW WE DID IT To dice a mango, you'll first have to remove the flesh of the fruit from its large, flat seed. With a large, sharp knife, cut the fruit vertically, sliding the knife along the seed on one side. Repeat on the other side, which will give you 2 large pieces. Remove the peel from the pieces and dice the flesh.

2 cups **water**

1 cup **whole-wheat couscous**

2 teaspoons **olive oil**

¾ teaspoon **salt**

⅛ teaspoon freshly **ground pepper**

1 ripe **mango**, peeled and diced

⅓ cup seeded and finely diced **red bell pepper**

¼ cup thinly sliced **scallions**

2 tablespoons chopped **fresh cilantro**

1 tablespoon **rice-wine vinegar**

½ teaspoon grated **orange zest**

CHAPTER 9

Refreshing Endings

Fresh Berries with Lime Ricotta and Balsamic Drizzle

PREP	10 MINUTES PLUS 5 MINUTES COOLING TIME
COOK	ABOUT 5 MINUTES
SERVES	4

½ cup **balsamic vinegar**

1 cup **fat-free ricotta cheese**

2 teaspoons grated **lime** or **lemon zest**

1 pint **fresh strawberries**

1 (6-ounce) container **fresh raspberries** or **blackberries**

1 (6-ounce) container **fresh blueberries**

1 Bring the vinegar to a boil in a medium saucepan; boil rapidly until it is reduced to about ¼ cup, about 4 minutes. Remove from the heat and let cool 5 minutes.

2 Meanwhile, place the cheese in a food processor (a small processor is fine for this amount) or blender and process until smooth and creamy. Scrape into a serving bowl and sprinkle with the lime zest.

3 Stand the bowl of whipped ricotta in the center of a large serving platter. Arrange the berries around the bowl. Drizzle the berries with the reduced balsamic and serve at once.

PER SERVING (¼ of fruit with ¼ cup ricotta): 137 Cal, 1 g Fat, 0 g Sat Fat, 0 g Trans Fat, 10 mg Chol, 76 mg Sod, 26 g Carb, 6 g Fib, 6 g Prot, 133 mg Calc. **POINTS** value: **2.**

EXPRESS LANE If you have a good-quality aged balsamic vinegar—by all means use it. Aged balsamic is so thick and luscious-tasting, you won't need to bother reducing or cooling it, so you'll only need ¼ cup for the recipe.

Fresh Berries with Lime Ricotta
and Balsamic Drizzle

Cantaloupe Fans with Raspberry-Vanilla Sauce

PREP	20 MINUTES
COOK	NONE
SERVES	4

2 (6-ounce) containers fresh **raspberries** or 1½ cups frozen, thawed

2 teaspoons **vanilla extract**

1 teaspoon fresh **lemon juice**

1 small ripe **cantaloupe**

4 sprigs **fresh mint**

Edible flowers, such as impatiens, jasmine, or honeysuckle (optional)

1 Pick out and reserve about 12 raspberries and set aside for garnish. Combine the remaining raspberries, the vanilla, and lemon juice in a blender. Process on high speed until smooth, about 2 minutes. Strain the mixture into a bowl through a wire mesh sieve, pressing with a rubber spatula; discard the seeds.

2 Cut the cantaloupe in half lengthwise and scoop out the seeds. Cut each half into 6 long wedges and remove the rind. With a small sharp knife, make 4 or 5 lengthwise cuts down each wedge almost to the end, leaving one end intact to serve as the base of the fan. Press gently to open each fan.

3 Pour about ¼ cup of the raspberry sauce on each of 4 plates, top each with 3 cantaloupe fans and sprinkle with the reserved fresh raspberries. Garnish with the mint and flowers (if using).

PER SERVING (1 plate): 86 Cal, 1 g Fat, 0 g Sat Fat, 0 g Trans Fat, 0 mg Chol, 10 mg Sod, 19 g Carb, 7 g Fib, 2 g Prot, 34 mg Calc.
POINTS value: *1.*

GOOD IDEA You can substitute other melons such as honeydew, Galia, or Crenshaw for the cantaloupe.

Sautéed Bananas with Vanilla Frozen Yogurt

PREP	10 MINUTES
COOK	ABOUT 5 MINUTES
SERVES	6

1 tablespoon **unsalted butter**

3 tablespoons packed **light brown sugar**

3 tablespoons **orange juice**

¼ cup **raisins**

1 teaspoon **vanilla extract**

¼ teaspoon **cinnamon**

⅛ teaspoon **ground nutmeg**

3 firm-ripe **bananas,** peeled and cut on an angle into ½-inch-thick slices

2 cups **vanilla fat-free frozen yogurt**

1 Melt the butter in a medium nonstick skillet over medium-high heat. Add the sugar, orange juice, and raisins; cook, stirring occasionally, until the sugar has dissolved, about 1 minute. Stir in the vanilla, cinnamon, and nutmeg and cook about 30 seconds. Add the bananas and cook, stirring occasionally, until softened, 2–3 minutes.

2 Place ⅓ cup of the yogurt in each of 6 wine glasses or dessert bowls and top with ⅓ cup of the banana mixture. Serve at once.

PER SERVING (1 glass): 201 Cal, 2 g Fat, 1 g Sat Fat, 0 g Trans Fat, 6 mg Chol, 52 mg Sod, 44 g Carb, 1 g Fib, 4 g Prot, 122 mg Calc. **POINTS** value: **4.**

GOOD IDEA When selecting bananas for this recipe, look for yellow ones that are still a bit firm so that they hold their shape when cooked; overripe bananas tend to fall apart during cooking.

Banana Brown Rice Pudding

Banana Brown Rice Pudding

PREP	10 MINUTES PLUS ABOUT 30 MINUTES COOLING TIME
COOK	ABOUT 20 MINUTES
SERVES	4

1 cup cooked **brown rice**

1 cup **fat-free milk**

Pinch **salt**

1 ripe **banana**, mashed

1 teaspoon **vanilla extract**

¼ teaspoon **cinnamon**

⅛ teaspoon **almond extract**

1 Combine the rice, milk, and salt in a medium saucepan; bring to a boil. Reduce the heat and simmer uncovered, stirring occasionally, until slightly thickened, about 15 minutes. Let the mixture cool to room temperature about 30 minutes.

2 Stir in the banana, vanilla, cinnamon, and almond extract.

PER SERVING (⅓ cup): 106 Cal, 1 g Fat, 0 g Sat Fat, 0 g Trans Fat, 1 mg Chol, 69 mg Sod, 22 g Carb, 2 g Fib, 4 g Prot, 82 mg Calc. **POINTS** value: *2.*

GOOD IDEA This pudding is best served at room temperature. But if you wish to refrigerate it, do so for no longer than 1 day and cover the surface directly with plastic wrap to prevent discoloration of the banana.

Cinnamon S'mores

PREP	10 MINUTES
COOK	ABOUT 8 MINUTES
SERVES	8

8 whole low-fat **honey graham crackers** (4 rectangles per cracker)

¾ cup **marshmallow fluff**

4 tablespoons cup **semisweet chocolate chips**

⅛ teaspoon **cinnamon**

8 (12 x 6-inch) sheets **foil**

1 Preheat the oven to 425°F.

2 Spread 4 of the crackers each with 3 tablespoons of the marshmallow fluff. Top each with 1 tablespoon of the chocolate chips and sprinkle with the cinnamon. Top each with another cracker. Cut each cracker in half, making 8 sandwiches.

3 Place each sandwich in the center of a sheet of foil and wrap, making 8 packages. Set the packages on a baking sheet and bake until hot and melted, about 8 minutes. Open the packages carefully and serve at once.

PER SERVING (1 package): 161 Cal, 3 g Fat, 1 g Sat Fat, 0 g Trans Fat, 0 mg Chol, 192 mg Sod, 33 g Carb, 1 g Fib, 2 g Prot, 8 mg Calc.
POINTS value: *3.*

DEFINITION According to the Girl Scouts of America, s'mores is an abbreviated version of "gimme-some-more" and refers to campfire-roasted marshmallows. Although the origin of the cookie version of s'mores is unclear, the first published recipe appeared in the 1927 Girl Scout handbook. No matter what the origin, we're mighty thankful for this yummy treat!

Cinnamon S'mores

Microwave Apple Crisp

PREP	10 MINUTES
COOK	8–9 MINUTES
SERVES	6

4 Golden Delicious, McIntosh, Gala, or Braeburn **apples**, peeled and thinly sliced

4 tablespoons packed **light brown sugar**

¾ teaspoon **cinnamon**

¼ teaspoon **ground nutmeg**

1 cup **low-fat granola**

1 tablespoon **butter**, melted

1 Spray an 8-inch square microwavable dish with nonstick spray. Combine the apples, 3 tablespoons of the sugar, ½ teaspoon of the cinnamon, and the nutmeg in a bowl; mix well. Transfer the apple mixture to the baking dish.

2 Combine the granola, butter, remaining 1 tablespoon sugar, and remaining ¼ teaspoon cinnamon in a bowl; mix well. Sprinkle the granola mixture evenly over the apples. Microwave, uncovered, on High until the apples are tender and bubbling, 8–9 minutes.

PER SERVING (⅙ of crisp): 190 Cal, 3 g Fat, 1 g Sat Fat, 0 g Trans Fat, 5 mg Chol, 56 mg Sod, 42 g Carb, 4 g Fib, 2 g Prot, 24 mg Calc. **POINTS** value: **3.**

GOOD IDEA Try the crisp with a scoop of your favorite fat-free frozen yogurt (½ cup vanilla fat-free frozen yogurt will increase the **POINTS** value by 2).

Tropical Smoothie with Ginger

PREP	15 MINUTES
COOK	NONE
SERVES	2

Place the mango, pineapple, strawberries, ice cubes, lime juice, ginger, and sugar in a blender; blend on high speed, stopping the blender occasionally to push the fruit and uncrushed ice cubes down with the handle of a wooden spoon, until smooth. Serve at once, garnished with the mint.

PER SERVING (1 cup): 123 Cal, 1 g Fat, 0 g Sat Fat, 0 g Trans Fat, 0 mg Chol, 4 mg Sod, 32 g Carb, 4 g Fib, 1 g Prot, 24 mg Calc.
POINTS value: **2.**

GOOD IDEA Chop some additional fresh strawberries to float on top of each smoothie for another colorful garnish.

1 fresh **mango**, peeled, pitted, and cut in large chunks

1 cup fresh **pineapple cubes**

½ cup halved **fresh strawberries**

½ cup **ice cubes**

2 teaspoons fresh **lime juice**

1 teaspoon grated peeled **fresh ginger**

½ teaspoon **sugar**

2 small sprigs **fresh mint,** for garnish

Coffee Frappé

Coffee Frappé

PREP	5 MINUTES PLUS 15 MINUTES CHILLING TIME
COOK	NONE
SERVES	1

Combine the coffee, milk, banana, vanilla, sugar, and cardamom (if using) in a blender and blend at high speed until smooth and frothy. Serve in a tall glass with a cinnamon stick as a stirrer.

PER SERVING (1⅓ cups): 114 Cal, 1 g Fat, 0 g Sat Fat, 0 g Trans Fat, 3 mg Chol, 67 mg Sod, 22 g Carb, 1 g Fib, 5 g Prot, 157 mg Calc.
POINTS** value: **2.

GOOD IDEA Serve this slightly sweet-and-spicy, chilled coffee over ice, or not, as you prefer.

½ cup chilled **brewed espresso** or **strong dark roast coffee**

½ cup **fat-free milk**

½ ripe **banana**

¾ teaspoon **vanilla extract**

½ teaspoon **sugar**

⅛ teaspoon **ground cardamom** or **cinnamon** (optional)

1 long **cinnamon stick**

Apples with Goat Cheese and Honey

PREP	10 MINUTES
COOK	25–35 SECONDS
SERVES	4

3 **Gala** or **Golden Delicious apples**, cut into ¼-inch-thick slices

1 tablespoon **fresh lemon juice**

2 ounces **goat cheese**, crumbled

3 tablespoons **honey**

1 Combine the apples and lemon juice in a bowl; toss well to coat. Arrange the apples in overlapping concentric circles on a large round platter. Sprinkle with the cheese.

2 Place the honey in a small microwavable bowl and heat in the microwave until warm and easy to pour, 25–35 seconds. Drizzle the honey over the apples and serve at once.

PER SERVING (¼ of platter): 162 Cal, 5 g Fat, 3 g Sat Fat, 0 g Trans Fat, 11 mg Chol, 74 mg Sod, 29 g Carb, 2 g Fib, 3 g Prot, 51 mg Calc.
POINTS value: **3.**

GOOD IDEA Depending on the season, try this dessert with pears, plums, peaches, or nectarines.

Fruity Chicken Salad, page 59

Tofu, Asparagus, and Mushroom "Risotto", page 208

Dry and Liquid Measurement Equivalents

If you are converting the recipes in this book to metric measurements, use the following chart as a guide.

TEASPOONS	TABLESPOONS	CUPS	FLUID OUNCES
3 teaspoons	1 tablespoon		½ fluid ounce
6 teaspoons	2 tablespoons	⅛ cup	1 fluid ounce
8 teaspoons	2 tablespoons plus 2 teaspoons	⅙ cup	
12 teaspoons	4 tablespoons	¼ cup	2 fluid ounces
15 teaspoons	5 tablespoons	⅓ cup minus 1 teaspoon	
16 teaspoons	5 tablespoons plus 1 teaspoon	⅓ cup	
18 teaspoons	6 tablespoons	¼ cup plus 2 tablespoons	3 fluid ounces
24 teaspoons	8 tablespoons	½ cup	4 fluid ounces
30 teaspoons	10 tablespoons	½ cup plus 2 tablespoons	5 fluid ounces
32 teaspoons	10 tablespoons plus 2 teaspoons	⅔ cup	
36 teaspoons	12 tablespoons	¾ cup	6 fluid ounces
42 teaspoons	14 tablespoons	1 cup minus 2 tablespoons	7 fluid ounces
45 teaspoons	15 tablespoons	1 cup minus 1 tablespoon	
48 teaspoons	16 tablespoons	1 cup	8 fluid ounces

VOLUME	
¼ teaspoon	1 milliliter
½ teaspoon	2 milliliters
1 teaspoon	5 milliliters
1 tablespoon	15 milliliters
2 tablespoons	30 milliliters
3 tablespoons	45 milliliters
¼ cup	60 milliliters
⅓ cup	80 milliliters
½ cup	120 milliliters
⅔ cup	160 milliliters
¾ cup	175 milliliters
1 cup	240 milliliters
1 quart	950 milliliters

LENGTH	
1 inch	25 millimeters
1 inch	2.5 centimeters

WEIGHT	
1 ounce	30 grams
¼ pound	120 grams
½ pound	240 grams
1 pound	480 grams

OVEN TEMPERATURE

250°F	120°C	400°F	200°C
275°F	140°C	425°F	220°C
300°F	150°C	450°F	230°C
325°F	160°C	475°F	250°C
350°F	180°C	500°F	260°C
375°F	190°C	525°F	270°C

NOTE: Measurement of less than ⅛ teaspoon is considered a dash or a pinch. Metric volume measurements are approximate.

Index

POINTS value Recipe Index

Citrus Chicken Breasts, 137

Cranberry-Pear Chicken, 148

Dijon Beef Stroganoff, 95

Easiest Tortilla Chicken Soup, 41

Fresh Cream of Tomato Soup, 47

Fruity Chicken Salad, 59

Grilled Calamari with Arugula and Tomatoes, 21

Grilled Flank Steak with Chimichurri, 89

Herbed Salmon Burgers with Tomato Salsa, 180

Hunan Lamb, 126

Lamb Chops with Mango-Mint Salsa, 130

Lamb Chops with Roasted Garlic Aïoli, 127

Microwave Herbed Cod with Tomato Sauce, 190

Microwave Moroccan Chicken Stew, 150

Microwaved Pork and Beans, 122

Pasta e Fagioli, 228

Roasted Root Vegetables, 254

Salmon on a Bed of Kale, 177

Sautèed Bananas with Vanilla Frozen Yogurt, 271

Shrimp-Basil Tabbouleh Salad, 67

Smoked Chicken, Tea, and Noodle Soup, 39

Smoked Turkey with Creamy Carrot and Raisin Salad, 61

Smoky Beans and Rice, 223

Snapper with Cilantro Sauce, 188

Steak au Poivre, 90

Sukiyaki Salad, 92

Sweet-and-Sour Veal Cutlets, 104

Tandoori Chicken Thighs, 164

Tarragon Chicken with 40 Cloves of Garlic, 136

Tarragon Turkey Burgers, 171

Tofu, Asparagus, and Mushroom "Risotto", 208

Tropical Chicken Salad, 168

Tuscan-Style Chicken Thighs, 155

Vegetable Paella, 229

Vichyssoise with Olive-Egg Garnish, 55

5 POINTS value

Barbecue Salmon with Ginger, 179

Beef Creole, 101

Beef, Rice, and Root Vegetable Soup, 34

Buffalo Chicken Salad with Buttermilk-Blue Cheese Dressing, 140

Bulgur Pilaf with Roasted Tomatoes, Chickpeas, and Spinach, 233

Cajun Blackened Salmon, 176

Caribbean Black Beans and Chicken, 151

Catfish Florentine en Papillote, 194

Chicken Souvlaki with Rice and Yogurt Sauce, 159

Couscous-Stuffed Leg of Lamb, 125

Creamy Cannellini Bean Soup, 50

Cuban Beans and Rice, 224

Dilled Beet and White Bean Salad, 70

Fajitas, 99

Fajita-Style Skillet Pork, 109

Fennel-and-Onion Smothered Steak, 87

Fresh Corn Chowder, 52

Frittata with Sun-Dried Tomatoes, Chard, and Leeks, 210

Fruited Couscous and Ham Salad, 62

Garlicky Fish and Bread Soup, 191

Ham and Egg Frittata, 119

Herb-Roasted Chicken, 135

Mediterranean Shrimp and Scallop Salad, 200

Moo Shu Veggie Fajitas, 237

Pork Chops with Pear Sauce, 114

Prime Rib with Mushroom Sauce, 85

Quick Chicken Mole, 153

Red Snapper Cakes with Nectarine-Citrus Salad, 187

Roast Pork with Root Vegetables, 106

Roasted Halibut with Lemon Dressing, 198

Shortcut Chicken Picadillo, 165

Shrimp and Cabbage Chowder, 42

Sicilian Cod with Zucchini, 192

Slow-Cooker Veal and Bean Soup, 37

Spaghetti and Meatballs, 103

Spicy Shrimp Fried Rice, 202

Steak and Potatoes, 84

Teriyaki Pork Stir-Fry, 111

Thai Beef Sauté, 91

Vietnamese Caramel Pork with Black Pepper, 108

Warm Salmon Salad with Buttermilk-Scallion Dressing, 63

White Chili, 112

6 POINTS value

Barbecued Pressure-Cooker Pork, 118

Beef Bourguignon in a Flash, 94

Bistro Pork Sauté, 115

BLT Chicken and Corn Chowder, 167

Bouillabaisse, 203

Chicken Cacciatore, 138

Chicken Paprikash, 162

Notes

Notes

Notes

Notes